D1270513

THE BOY BEHIND
THE DOOR

HOW SALOMON KOOL ESCAPED THE NAZIS.
INSPIRED BY A TRUE STORY

DAVID TABATSKY

ап

ISBN 9789493276338 (ebook)

ISBN 9789493276314 (paperback)

ISBN 9789493276321 (hardcover)

Publisher: Amsterdam Publishers, The Netherlands

info@amsterdampublishers.com

The Boy Behind the Door is part of the series **Holocaust Books For Young Adults**

FOREWORD

Several years ago, I was introduced to Sanford Batkin, an American businessman living in Scarsdale, New York. He had been active in the Jewish community for a long time and had a special story he wanted to tell.

In the late 1970s, Sandy and his wife went on a vacation to Aruba, a small island in what is known as the Dutch Caribbean. They met Sal and Nettie Kool, a couple from the Netherlands, who were also on holiday. One day, while standing in the ocean, Sal poured out his astounding story to Sandy – how, as a young teenager, he had survived the Nazi occupation of his country during World War II. It was the first time Sal had ever shared this part of his life with anyone outside of Amsterdam, and Sandy was flabbergasted. The two men and their wives became friends. They continued to meet over the years, and grew even closer.

As their friendship deepened, Sal's story of survival continued to haunt Sandy. He urged Sal to share his entire ordeal, not just with his sons living In Israel but with a new generation who didn't know much about what had happened during the Holocaust. Sandy encouraged Sal to write a book but Sal, a shy and private man, wasn't too keen on the idea and did not know how to even begin.

That's where I came in. Sandy asked me if I would go to

Amsterdam and work with Sal to tell his story. I was fortunate to spend such a lovely and meaningful time with Sal and Nettie, as they hosted me for many meals, and Sal and I retraced his young life through the streets of Amsterdam, the city where he was born and raised and forced to escape before finally returning at the end of the war.

What follows here is the result of our combined efforts to tell this extraordinary story. All of it is based entirely on real events and real people.

1

"Sal, get back in here!"

My mother was shouting at me, as usual. She wasn't mean but her voice was probably loud enough to be heard ten blocks away. It was nine o'clock on a Sunday morning, when most 12-year-old boys in my neighborhood were heading out of their homes to meet their friends.

I wasn't any different. I was shorter than average, that's for sure, and baby-faced, too but I was a regular kid. And on that beautiful spring day, I had one thing on my mind when I woke up. I just wanted to hop on my bicycle and ride.

I threw on my favorite pants and headed downstairs, stopping at the front door of our apartment so I could see if my best friend, Frank, was outside yet, waiting for me.

"Sal!" My mother was calling me from the kitchen.

"Be right there." I looked down the long stairway but couldn't see Frank.

"Salomon, I'm calling you!"

Rachel Winter, my dear mother, was a force to be reckoned with, especially in her kitchen, also known as her command center, bustling around in her favorite apron, the one with the Dutch tulips printed brightly down the front. With her thick, shoulder-length hair waving around her delicate face, moving swiftly from the stove to the sink and back, her slippers flapping against her heels, she was a sight to behold.

And on that day, like most others in 1939, my mother was generating not only breakfast for our entire family but the beginnings of lunch and dinner, too. But none of that kept her from keeping strict track of me, Salomon Kool, her youngest son, known by everyone as Sal.

"Where do you think you're going?"

I ambled into her headquarters, grabbed a piece of bread, and started toward the door. "Mama, it's Easter Sunday. I don't have gymnastics today. Frank will be waiting outside for me any minute and–"

"Since when do you eat standing up, making crumbs on my floor?"

"I don't know."

I stammered, noticing that the bread wasn't particularly tasty. I was so anxious to get outside I'd forgotten to put anything on it.

For a kid growing up in Amsterdam, in the Netherlands, riding a bike came with the territory. It was practically a birthright. Everybody had one – kids and parents alike – and they weren't meant to be stored away in the basement. Bicycles were intended for riding, and that morning I was itching to get outside and blast through my neighborhood, bouncing from one narrow street to the other, over one canal bridge and under the next, racking up a series of stories I could share with my schoolmates on Monday morning.

"And since when is that breakfast for a growing boy?" She looked sadly at my lonely piece of bread.

"I don't know. Since, five minutes ago?" I had no idea what I was even saying.

"What's your plan, Sal?" My mother grabbed the bread out of my hand and slapped a fresh, hotly buttered piece of toast in its place.

"Uh..."

"Take this one," she said. "Toast is only good when it's hot."

"Thanks, Mama." I smiled.

When she was right, which she usually was, you knew it.

"And drink this, too." She handed me a mug of hot tea, caressed my cheek, and went right back to her business in the kitchen. She might've been annoying sometimes but she sure knew how to make good toast. And the sweetest tea, too.

As I strolled to the front door of our apartment, licking the jam off the top of the butter, I looked down the stairway and through the open entryway of the building. I could see my new bicycle, perched against the wall, just waiting for me to finish eating and begin my adventure.

The bike itself wasn't actually new. I had inherited it from my older brother, Louis, but it seemed to me like it came straight from the best bicycle shop in Amsterdam. I didn't care that it had a worn-down seat, taped up handlebars, and tires as bald as our Rabbi's head. When my father surprised me the night before with the hand-me-down, I knew right away that I was in a new league. It did not look like a little kid's bike, and everybody would recognize that.

"Sal!" Frank was booming at me from the street. "Are you coming?" His face was poking into the open landing of our building, looking straight up the stairs.

"Hold on a second." I signaled that I'd be down in a minute. "Bye, Mama." I hoped that if I said it softly and quickly enough that she might not notice.

"Salomon Winter, don't you dare set foot outside my house without permission!"

"But Mama..."

"Sal, don't try to sweet sweet-talk me; you're still a child."

"I'm not a kid anymore! I'm almost 12!" I shouted at her to make my point.

"Well, that's true," she said, standing to her full height of five-feet-four-inches. "But until you can look me in the eye and tell me you're a young man, you're still a boy and I still make the rules around here." With that declaration, she turned back to the stove, leaving me standing there like a short kid without a prayer. "And your friend Frank shouldn't be yelling so loud. He'll wake up everybody."

"Mama, I'll be 12 in less than a month. Come on, let me go, will you?" I pleaded, trying not to whine but reminding her how

3

important it was that I leave the house immediately. "Frank is waiting. Look out of the window if you don't believe me."

"Frank! Frank! Frank! All I hear is Frank!"

"He's my best friend, and together we're almost 24 years old, so we won't get in trouble. Promise. Besides, I don't have gymnastics today, and my coach says I need exercise."

"Just a minute, Mr. Young Man with the Baby Face. Let me think. Can a mother have a minute to think, please?"

"Uh, yeah, go ahead and think." I was afraid of what that might mean.

"Just tell your friend, Frank, that your fair-minded, thoughtful, generous general of a mother is thinking." And then she went right back to work.

I loved my mother. Don't get me wrong. I mean she was the best but on most Sunday mornings, I would have already kissed her goodbye and been out of the apartment before the rest of my family was even awake. I always arrived at the gymnasium promptly by eight o'clock.

"Still thinking, Mama?"

"Still thinking," she said, smiling at me. "Mr. Short Young Man with the big ideas."

I was four inches shorter than my mother, so I had to agree with her on that but I was quick and nimble, if I do say so, myself.

"You know I can keep up with all the big boys down at the gym." I figured that this fact would clinch my immediate departure.

"Hmm, so I've heard from Mr. Koen."

"And now, with my bike from Louis, I can go with Frank, and you don't have to worry, okay?"

"Sal, it's 1939. Last time I checked, that makes you still a boy. In one year, when you have your Bar Mitzvah, you can ride on your own."

"Oh God! Mama!"

No response.

"God!" I repeated it for effect but it didn't work.

"Watch your mouth, Salomon."

I stared. "What?"

4

She said it as if I had something to say. Of course, I didn't, because how could I explain that although I was taking the Lord's name in vain, in this case it was okay because it was a matter of life and death?

"Sal? Are you coming, or what?"

We both heard Frank, still waiting for me.

"Okay, Sal, it's such a nice day I'm going to let you go for a little ride with your lovely friend, Frank."

I started jumping for joy.

"But!"

"But? How come there's always a 'but'?"

"Why? I'll tell you. Because I'm your mother, and you're to go no further than three blocks from this apartment, in any direction. And don't think for a minute I don't have people watching who will tell me if you go even one block past that."

I chewed on the last corner of my toast and thought long and hard about her offer. The rules basically left Frank and me the chance to play ring-around-the-rosy on our bicycles, not an especially adventurous prospect for two (almost) 12-year-olds. I knew my mother worried about me riding around on the busy streets but I wished she might've loved me a little bit less that morning and not cared so much about my every move.

"Mama, I have an idea." I was stalling until I could think of one.

And then Louis staggered right by me on his way into the kitchen. He patted me on the top of my head and swiped the last piece of toast right out of my mouth.

If I hadn't admired my brother like I did, I might've been really upset at losing my last bite of breakfast. But Louis had appeared at the perfect moment, and I wasted no time seizing the opportunity.

"Hey Louis," I whispered. "What are you doing today?"

"Uh, I don't know. Nothing planned."

He greeted our mother with a kiss on top of her head. Louis was already 13, and at five-foot-nine, he towered over her. "Morning, Mama."

"You're up early. Feeling energetic today?"

"I feel fine, but Frank woke me up, yelling like a sick dog for Sal to come downstairs."

"See what I told you?" Mama said.

"Hey Sal!" It was Frank. Again.

"See you later!"

What was I going to do? Frank's mother was letting him ride around on his own. He was three months older than me. I needed another plan.

Louis took my mug of tea, downed a gulp, and handed it back to me like we were a comedy team from the Dutch Variety Theater. "Thank you, Sal." He was so cheerful he just sounded dumb. "What delicious tea you've made this morning."

A light bulb went on. Louis was the key to getting my mother to let me go for a real bike ride. If he agreed, how could she say no?

"I have an idea."

"You and your ideas, Sal."

She turned to me with a pot in one hand and half a chicken in the other. "I just said you could go with Frank. What now?"

"Frank's probably far away by now."

I stepped toward the refrigerator. My mother cut me off. I froze. She saw me staring at the chicken in her hand, as if I was waiting for her to slug me with it. Then, Louis made these chicken sounds and she laughed.

"Okay, okay, the two of you can go ride together. That means you, too, Louis. You get to ride the brand-new bike your father just bought you. And don't forget how hard he worked to buy you that bike."

Louis nodded, knowing she was right.

"But!"

"But? Again? Another but?"

"Sal, you can go with Louis, provided he never lets you out of his sight."

I hugged my mother really hard and pulled Louis out of the kitchen toward the front door. He pretended to protest.

"Shut up, Louis; you're dressed, let's go."

"Wait a minute." He was laughing as I kept trying to push him out the door. Louis pointed back in the direction of our mother. We ran back into the kitchen, grabbed some more toast off the counter and shoved a couple of apples into our pockets.

"Bye, Mama!"

Louis and I ran down the steps. "See you when we get back!"

I felt like we had to get out of there before she changed her mind.

"Don't hurt the chicken!" Louis screamed, as he jumped on his bike and sped off.

I rode off as fast as I could, bouncing down the famous cobblestone streets of Amsterdam. Louis was already half a block ahead of me but I didn't care. I wasn't exactly on my own but it was the next best thing.

2

Louis and I rounded the next corner at top speed and nearly ran over our father, returning home from his morning errands.

"Hi, Papa!" I was pedaling as fast as I could.

"Bye, Papa!" Louis yelled out, riding just ahead of me. "Thanks for the new bike!" He didn't even look back.

"Thanks for mine, too!" My voice trailed in the breeze as we crossed the canal bridge, leaving our father standing on the sidewalk, smiling as his two boys sped off, satisfied with their new bicycles.

I could almost hear him, saying, "Ach, what about these sweets I bought for you? They're not cheap, you know, and money is tight these days, and, oh never mind."

I bet he grabbed one out of the bag, took a big bite, and continued walking home. Papa was five-foot-eight and quite trim so a few sweets wouldn't affect his waistline.

He must've been amused by Louis and me, flying right by him on our bikes. But not completely and not for long. He was aware of things we didn't know or care to understand. Under his arm, my father carried the morning newspaper with its ominous reports of bad news coming right next door from Germany and the rest of Europe.

Just a month ago, Hitler's troops had entered Czechoslovakia.

Days later, they turned Slovakia into a satellite territory of Nazi Germany. Fascist governments were in control in Spain and Italy. The day would come, my father feared, when we might not be free to ride our bikes through the streets of Amsterdam. Life for the Jews of Europe might be forever changed if current events continued. The time was approaching, slowly but surely, when conditions would worsen, and our freedoms would significantly disappear. Papa was usually cheerful, especially when I was little, but he had become more and more serious in the last year.

As a member of the diamond workers trade union, my father was socially and politically active, and he knew that it was just a matter of time before the situation would change. He was a worrier, and we recognized it every time we saw him scratching his head and running his left hand through his thick, dark hair. But my father was a realist, he said, and felt like he had good reason. Every time he heard the worsening news from Germany, he grew more convinced that it was going to spread across the border and that we would not be able to do anything to stop it.

At that time, Dutch society was divided into four major groups, known as pillars: Catholics, Protestants, Socialists and Liberals. Each of them had distinctive social, political and economic beliefs. Normally, these tightly knit networks had little interaction with each other. From the cradle to the grave, people of the same pillar remained within their own circle.

Dutch Jews were either Socialists or Liberals, and during the 1920s and most of the 1930s barriers to Jews were especially relaxed. My father had grown up in a more permissive society. But two decades can't entirely erase generations of deep-seated prejudices, so by the end of the 1930s, when German socialist principles under the Nazi Party spread throughout Europe, Dutch society too began to change for the worse, and traditional democratic socialists like my father were keenly aware of the dangers these changes presented for the Jews of the Netherlands.

While Louis and I rode on, we exchanged thoughts about our father. An intelligent and sensitive man, and normally full of good humor, he had been growing increasingly cynical, angry, and depressed, and as much as he didn't want to, he couldn't help exposing his feelings to his own family.

I admired and loved my father but on that beautiful spring morning I rode my bike without a care in the world, except for keeping up with Louis. Amsterdam was home sweet home but like any boy in the world my age, I was only interested in riding as fast and as far as I could. And since I was a lot smaller, I had to pedal twice as hard!

3

As we entered the woods along Vondelpark, Louis began to pedal further ahead. He disappeared into the trees, darting between them, which made it seem like I was momentarily alone. This cat-and-mouse game continued to intensify until we came to a small hill overlooking the southern end of the city.

Louis stopped and smiled. "Why don't we go to Eindhoven?"

Our family had lived there before moving to Amsterdam, and Louis and I had fond memories of our first childhood home.

"Are you kidding me? Eindhoven is two hours away by train!"

Louis rolled his eyes, as if he expected to hear me go on and on with all my responsible reasons not to keep riding toward the darkened tree line and out of the city.

"It's a slow train," Louis said.

"What?"

"Oh, come on, Sal, what's the matter, little brother? Scared?"

While Louis sat on his bike, tying his shoes, and waiting for my answer, I sped off, making a lightning fast launch out of Amsterdam's city limits.

"Oh! Look at me! Who is Mama's boy now?"

I rode as fast as I could until nothing looked familiar anymore and I realized we were many kilometers away from our neighborhood. I figured we would have to turn back soon but for the moment I was thrilled, enjoying the lead I had over my brother.

I'd escaped the slow Sunday that must have been unfolding at home at mere human speed. If I'd been there, my mother would be nagging me to practice the cello. My father, after sharing his delicacies from the bakery, would've disappeared into his favorite lounge chair, lost in his books and newspapers. He'd emerge from his cocoon to share his thoughts that life, as we had known it up until then, was about to change, and not for the better, not at all.

What else is new?

That's what I would think to myself in moments like that.

What's the big deal?

My father was becoming obsessed with Hitler's plan to dominate Europe. As more and more Jews escaped antisemitic Germany and emigrated to Amsterdam, their stories convinced my father and his friends that the spread of the Nazi regime into our country was inevitable. But despite their best intentions, there was little any of them could do.

Over the past few months, my father had begun ranting and raving in front of our family. I wasn't a little boy anymore, and I was beginning to understand what he was talking about. What I didn't fully comprehend was explained to me by my older brothers and sister.

Although most of our family paid little attention to my father when he was in one of his "moods," his anger was enough to get my attention. I guessed that there had to be some credible reason for his behavior but if I thought about it for too long, I became frightened. I figured that my father, being so smart, must understand something about the world that my siblings and I did not. But I wasn't that interested in finding out what it was.

I was 12. Riding my bike was the only worldview I needed, and on that Sunday, I hadn't stopped pedaling since that pause on the hill in Vondelpark. Passing fields of newly blossoming tulips I breathed in the fragrant air and kept pedaling. As the setting sun began to change the bright white buds on the trees to a dull pink, I kept pedaling.

When I noticed more and more windmills on both sides of the road, I kept pedaling. I knew I was getting further and further away from home. I felt confused and intimidated by my new freedom, caught between my own ambitions and the cautioning voice of my parents. But I kept pedaling. Freedom!

Finally, when my legs couldn't go any more, I began to coast, and as I did, I looked back to see that Louis was out of breath but he had caught up to me.

"If we turn around now, Sal, it'll mean riding all the way back to Amsterdam."

"We don't have much choice then, do we?"

"Let's go! No one is here to stop us, so let's go!"

Louis and I smiled at each other, thoroughly enjoying the freedom our bicycle ride was offering. Far away from our daily lives in Amsterdam, we felt liberated by the fresh air and wide-open spaces. Although we were a long distance away from home, we both considered ourselves to be perfectly safe in the countryside. The crazy notion of cycling all the way to Eindhoven had become unexpectedly real.

With some mysterious burst of energy, we pushed on. It didn't seem long before we crossed the railroad tracks into the familiar village and entered our old neighborhood. Long after dark, we coasted into the yard of the Vissers, our old family friends.

They welcomed us with delight but I felt a new and strange feeling, something like loneliness. I couldn't wait to hear my mother's voice, no matter how angry she might be.

Once inside the house, Louis and I had a cup of warm milk. Before I could even finish mine, I asked to use the telephone to call home. When Mama heard my voice and realized I was safe and sound in Eindhoven, she instantly switched from crying to scolding, as if someone had written it down already in a play script she was acting. I held the phone out so Louis could hear her tirade. He just laughed silently, probably glad she was yelling at me and not him.

Papa seemed less concerned, and I could almost see him smiling through the receiver. Louis and I had dodged a serious bullet.

As I collapsed into a very welcome bed in the guestroom I felt that my relationship with my parents was now somehow different, on a telephone, in the dark, 130 kilometers away from home. I felt an odd, new sense of personal freedom but it came with the same fear I had felt earlier, riding my bike through the darkening woods of my own city.

4

"Happy Birthday to Sal," they sang in loud, playful voices. "Happy Birthday to you!"

It was May 5, 1940, and I was now 13 years old. Birthdays are major events, and if anyone forgets, it's a big, fat blunder. My mother made sure everyone was there: aunts, uncles, cousins, family friends, and most important, Louis and Daniel, and of course, Tinie, doting on me as only an older sister can.

"Take your time, little brother," she whispered. "It's your choice."

"Make a wish, Sal, come on!"

Both of my brothers wrapped their arms around me, pressing me against the table where the cake was on display. I closed my eyes and prepared to blow out the candles. A slight smile must've been visible on my face, and Daniel wasted no time noticing.

"What's her name, Sal?"

"Oh, forget it, kid," said Louis. "If you have to wish for a girlfriend, it'll never happen."

"Leave him alone, boys," said Tinie. "Sal can have any girl he wants!"

I loved my sister. But in that moment, my mind was far away from any thoughts of girls. I was wishing for one thing, and one thing only – that every birthday I would ever have would be celebrated with all these people, together, as one big family. As I blew out the flames, and the house became totally dark for an instant, everyone cheered and applauded for me. They were happy to have a reason to assemble in our house and celebrate a joyous occasion. Even my father, when he could tear himself away from the radio, was part of the festivities.

Hitler's army had invaded Poland just eight months earlier, and he had promised he would not invade the Netherlands. What did he want with us, anyway? But just one month ago, Denmark and Norway had succumbed to the Germans. The governments of Belgium and England had warned our government that the Nazis would storm all three countries. Mussolini and Hitler had recently formed an alliance, pitting the armies of Germany and Italy against those of France and Britain. All the grown-ups talked about was the impending war.

During the past two weeks, the Dutch government had proclaimed martial law throughout the country. Local police were arresting members of the Dutch Nazi party, and just days ago, 21 prominent Nazi sympathizers had been arrested and jailed.

Why was everyone so upset? The Nazis couldn't just march in and take over whenever they wanted. The Dutch would never stand for that! We were a peace-loving people.

We knew that Europe was falling apart though. Even a kid my age could see that. My father found it increasingly difficult to enjoy family things like birthdays, especially mine, in my Bar Mitzvah year. I knew that he loved me, and all of us, but he hated the escalating war that seemed to be growing closer and closer to home.

We were barely finished eating my birthday cake when he burst into the room, paler than I'd ever seen him, staring at us like we were strangers on the street and not his beloved family.

"What is it, Papa?"

"The Norwegian government has escaped from Oslo and taken exile in London. I just heard it on the radio."

Suddenly the party was over, and our guests left. Which country would be next to fall to the Germans?

5

"Sal, come here, please."

My mother was calling me from the kitchen. "I need your help."

"Mama, I'm studying." I was in the sitting room, working hard.

"Sal! There's so much to do, with your Bar Mitzvah tomorrow."

"Exactly! I have a lot to study so I do it correctly."

"Oh, I'm sure you'll do fine. Listen to me. Louis is busy playing football, Daniel and Tinie are at work, and your father, God bless him, can't pull himself away from the radio."

"Mama!" I protested, but no luck.

"I want you to go across the street to the Kluiverts and ask Frank's mother if I can borrow her good lace tablecloth."

"Now? You need to know that right now?"

"What? You should go Saturday morning before we go to the synagogue?" She was trying to tease me. "Sal, do it now, please."

"But why can't Papa go? He loves talking with Mr. Kluivert about all this war stuff. They can go on and on for hours. Come on, Mama. Let Papa go. He'll be happy to ask instead of me."

Just then, my father walked into the kitchen, stiffly, looking like a ghost. His face was frozen and gray, like he was hypnotized. He stopped in the doorway as if someone else was controlling his legs. He didn't say a word. He didn't even look like a human being who could speak. He stared straight ahead at my mother, turned like a robot, and stared at me.

"Philip!" Mama was shocked at my father's appearance. "Oh my God, what is it?"

My father didn't move.

"What's wrong?"

My father said nothing and gazed blankly across the room.

"Philip, my darling, what is it?"

"Papa, say something!"

I stepped across the kitchen floor to him. "Papa! You're scaring Mama, and me, too."

He nodded his head back and forth. I once saw a man have a seizure in the marketplace and he did the same thing, rocking back and forth before he started to shake violently and collapsed to the ground. I was afraid the same thing could be happening to my father right there in our kitchen. I hoped he still knew me, standing there before him. I took his hand.

He looked down at me, swallowed hard, and lifted his eyes to the ceiling. "It's over."

"Philip, what are you saying?"

"What's over? What do you mean?"

"It's over. They've crossed the river."

"What are you talking about?"

"They've crossed the river and there's no turning back."

Mama looking down, as if she knew the answer.

My father didn't speak.

"Mama, who crossed the river? What river?"

"Philip, tell him."

My father took a long, slow breath, as if he was trying to breathe life back into himself after it had been taken away. He stood unsteadily, holding on to the table, like his legs might give way any second. "Hitler." He looked so pained saying that name out loud in front of us, as if he were violating our home by uttering that sound from his lips. "Adolf Hitler sent the German army across the Dutch border at the Waal River at 5:30 this morning and they are now marching toward Amsterdam."

18

"Oh my God!" My mother looked shocked, like I'd never see her.

"They're 70 kilometers away! What can we do?"

All I could think of was Louis and I, riding our bikes last year all the way to Eindhoven, 130 kilometers away. We were kids. If we could ride that far in one day, what could the German army do, marching with tanks?

"What can we do? I don't know, Rachel. I don't know. I don't know anything right now."

"We just have to wait and see, right Papa?"

I hoped my question sounded normal, because in that moment I felt desperate to make the German invasion seem like a problem we could fix, if only we put our minds to it.

"Yes, Sal. We can only wait and see what will happen."

My father turned and left the kitchen without saying another word. It was as if a judge had appeared out of nowhere in our house and ordered my father to be sent away to prison, or worse, to be put to death, and no words could change the verdict.

My mother and I looked at each other, unsure what to do. We both realized that my father would be sequestered in the bedroom, keeping his ears glued to the radio, and that if anything new should develop, we would be the first to hear about it.

"All right, then, Sal, I want you to go now and ask Mrs. Kluivert about her tablecloth." She was doing her best to put everything back to normal.

"Are you kidding me?"

"No, I am absolutely not doing anything of the sort. Hitler is 70 kilometers away, and while that may seem to be very close, meanwhile, life goes on here at home, and boys will have their Bar Mitzvahs, and tablecloths need to be borrowed, so just go across the street and take care of this like I asked you!"

I slipped on my shoes and left the apartment. Going downstairs, I couldn't get the picture of my father's ashen face out of my mind. Who even said the German army wants to come all the way to Amsterdam? Maybe they'll just stay in the south and relax by the river. But then again, maybe they won't.

As I stepped onto the sidewalk, I imagined what it would be like if

German tanks were rolling down the street. The thought made me shudder and hurry to see Frank. Surely his mother, who was a great cook, would have something sweet baking in the kitchen, and we could all have a good snack and think of better things, like tablecloths and Bar Mitzvahs.

But the mood inside the Kluivert's home wasn't any better. They had heard the news on the radio too, like most everybody in the city. Frank and his mother were quietly talking when I knocked on their door. I arranged to borrow the tablecloth, thanked Mrs. Kluivert, and returned home without so much as a single sweet. Things had to be pretty bad if Mrs. Kluivert wasn't handing out her famous cookies.

After a year of dreading the inevitable but mostly never imagining that such a bad dream could come true, it had finally happened. On Friday, May 10, 1940, Germany had invaded our country, just one day before my Bar Mitzvah.

6

The streets of our neighborhood were eerily quiet when we walked to the synagogue on Saturday morning. Only the occasional sound of a police siren could be heard. I was excited about my Bar Mitzvah but something didn't feel right and I didn't know exactly why.

"Hey, Sal, you nervous?" Louis gave me a little shove.

"Nothing to worry about, Sal, my boy," Daniel said. He wrapped his arm around me.

"Take it from me, your oldest and wisest brother. You'll do much better than I did."

"But you were terrific, Daniel!"

Tinie poked him in the ribs. "You even showed up on time!"

Daniel pushed Tinie into the empty street. Louis jumped off the sidewalk, pretending to rescue her.

"Help! Help! I'm being attacked! Help!"

I didn't want to be left out of the fun, even though I was nervous about doing a good job. I knew the prayers just fine but reciting them in front of everybody wasn't exactly my idea of a good time.

"Don't be afraid, little lady!"

I jumped and grabbed my sister with all the bravado I could muster. "I'll save you!" I struck a fighting pose, thinking I might even impress my brothers.

"Oh yeah, watch out," Louis said. "Look who's come to the rescue."

"I can't believe it!"

Daniel hid behind our mother.

"It's him!"

"Oh my God, no!" Louis cried. "It's him! Run for your life!"

"It's Bar Mitzvah Boy! Savior of the Universe!"

Daniel held on to Mama, and we all laughed loudly.

"I can't believe it. It's Bar Mitzvah boy, right here in Amsterdam!"

I was enjoying our game so much I didn't hear my father's voice behind us. "Enough."

"Oh, Bar Mitzvah Boy! You saved me!" Tinie pretended to fall into my arms. "You're my hero!"

As all four of us continued laughing, Papa repeated his order. "Enough."

We all heard him but didn't pay attention.

"Stop it!" He shouted and stepped into the street to pull me away "Stop! Do you hear me?" He pushed Daniel and Louis aside and pulled Tinie onto the sidewalk. His behavior was highly unusual, especially in public and on the Sabbath of all times.

"Philip," said Mama. "Let them be. It's a special day for all of us."

"Of course, it's a special day, but not for the reasons we'd like."

"Oh, not now, dear Philip. It's not often we can all be together like this, anymore. The children are getting older, and Sal is our last to become a Bar Mitzvah. Come, let them enjoy themselves. Let's all enjoy this day."

"How?"

My father bellowed in a way I'd never heard him yell before, as if he were mourning a terrible tragedy. He stopped in his tracks. "How can you expect me to enjoy myself when German soldiers are just hours away from Amsterdam?"

"Papa, please, we know what the radio is saying," said Daniel, "but it's a special day for Sal, and for all of us."

"Can we forget this war for a moment?" Tinie wrapped her arms around Papa. "Hmm, Papa? Surely the war can wait a minute while we have some fun."

We all wanted to believe that the war could wait while we lived our lives. We wanted to believe that the Germans would just change their minds and go away and march straight back across the border and leave us alone.

"Papa, the Germans can slow down while Sal reads the Torah," Louis said. "Once we finish the service and have something to eat, we'll tell them they can put their boots back on."

At first, Papa didn't say a word. We all stopped, just steps from the synagogue, waiting for him to say something so the tension could ease and we could go inside.

"Listen to me, all of you." He looked at us so sadly and tried to smile, as if the weight of the world was sitting heavily on his shoulders. "You're right. No matter what happens in the coming days and weeks, today is special. Today, my little boy becomes a man. And no one – I mean no one – is going to spoil that for us."

"Right, Papa, let's go already," said Daniel. "We don't want to be late."

"Late?" I said. "I can't be late. It's my Bar Mitzvah!" I skipped up the stairs into the synagogue, ready to be welcomed by many neighbors and friends. But only a handful of regulars had shown up, barely enough to fill a few pews. Frank and his parents stood nervously in the back, as if they expected the Nazis to barge in at any moment. The others sat expressionless, barely participating. Even the Rabbi wasn't his usual self, prowling about the pulpit as if he owned it. On that day, he sat motionless most of the time, as if his mind was far, far away.

I felt proud as I proceeded smoothly through the service, fulfilling my obligations without a hitch. Eyeing my father and mother, I knew that as the youngest child in our family and the last to become a Bar Mitzvah, my performance on this occasion carried extra importance. On top of that, with the Germans advancing into the Netherlands at record speed, our family and small circle of friends needed something positive to create a temporary distraction.

But that didn't last long. After the service, everyone offered hasty congratulations and quickly scattered. There would be no reception in the synagogue – no wine and cookies as there usually was for such a milestone. I would have to celebrate alone.

Immediately after the service, my father disappeared. Daniel and Tinie took off to work. Louis headed for a nearby park to play football. As Mama and I walked home through the silent streets, we barely spoke. Neither one of us chose to enter each other's thoughts. We could still feel the weight of my father's outburst on the way to the synagogue. Perhaps if it weren't spoken about, it would just quietly go away.

When we arrived at our apartment, we immediately smelled smoke.

"Mama, look out. Let me through!"

I moved her aside to get inside the front door of our building. It was as if I already knew my father was in serious trouble.

"Sal, no! Where are you going? Wait for me!" Mama tried to catch up to me on the stairway. "Where's your father?"

I followed the growing trail of smoke and found my father in the bathroom, pacing back and forth, soaked with sweat. In the bathtub, the large cloth banner, which had been hanging out of our living room window for the past two weeks, was now in flames. The thick letters, reading, VOTE SOCIALIST, were disappearing fast as the sheet continued to burn and turn black.

My father ignored me. He continued burning material in the bathtub. I was unsure what to say. I felt relieved he was safe but why was he burning a sign?

In a daze, he strode into the living room and returned with a pile of books and tossed them into the fire, one by one. They were political books, some of which my father had quoted from during family dinners. They were near and dear to him, so why burn them? Was there something wrong with owning them? How would anyone even know they were in our house?

We stood in the bathroom, watching and listening as the fire engulfed every book. Then, my father removed his Socialist Party member ID card from his wallet, rotated it round and round in his hand, and flicked it into the burning bathtub.

I watched my father's most important symbol disappear into the flames. Maybe if I didn't ask, I wouldn't have to hear more awful news. Papa's face, which had been red and flushed when I'd first found him in the bathroom, had now turned white.

After a long, long time, he finally spoke. "The Germans will march on Amsterdam tonight."

He said it calmly, without a trace of anger, as if he were acknowledging that there was nothing he could do about it.

"You mean with guns and tanks and real army stuff?"

I couldn't imagine it.

"Winston Churchill has become the new Prime Minister of England. The English are our friends but they have their own problems with the Germans, and they can't save us now, can they? We're all alone, here in the god-forsaken Netherlands."

"Papa, what do you mean?"

Although it was a warm spring day and the bathroom was hot from the fire, I suddenly felt an unmistakable chill.

"Well, my dear Bar Mitzvah boy, I'm sorry you're disappointed today. We all are but I'm afraid something much bigger than a boy's Bar Mitzvah is taking place, here and all over Europe. And we can't do much at all to stop it."

"Nothing?"

"I don't think so."

"Come on, I've had my Bar Mitzvah, so tell me the truth."

"The truth? You want the truth? I'll tell you if you really want to hear it. And why not? Soon, I won't be able to hide anything from you. The Germans have landed thousands and thousands of parachuting soldiers behind the lines of the Dutch Army."

"Stop joking, Papa."

"No, Sal, my dear. No joke."

"We can fight them back, can't we?"

"No, Sal. They're taking over all the strategic points in our country. The British are trying to help but they can't send enough men."

"We can fight them! The Dutch army is really good, right?"

"Yes, the Dutch army can fight, and they will. But there's little the Dutch soldiers will be able to do against the superior size and strength of the German army. They are ruthless. They will never stop until the Netherlands is under their power. The Nazis have done it this way in Poland and Austria and Denmark and Norway. What makes you think they can't do it here?"

"Okay, but why do you have to burn everything?"

"What other choice do I have?"

"Stop it, please! We just need a little bit of luck and things will change. You'll see."

"We'll need more than that! We'll need more good luck than we ever thought possible, and I'm afraid, my dear son, we've run totally out of that."

7

By the time I went to sleep, there was still no trace of the German army marching its way into Amsterdam. The streets were quiet. No one knew the Nazis' strategy and how soon they would enter the city.

I had never even met a German. I was in bed, thinking hard. Oh, but of course I had. Some new kids at school that year came from Germany. They were normal kids though. They had to learn to speak Dutch but we knew some German so we could communicate a few things between us, and we all got along. We were nice to them, and vice-versa. They had no reason to dislike us and tell people back in Germany that their army should attack us.

That was a silly idea, so I dropped it and fell asleep.

The next morning, my father decided it was safe for me to go to my weekly gymnastics class as I usually did. But walking on my normal path to the school, I sensed something different in the air. On a typical Sunday morning the streets were filled with people walking to their respective churches. Jewish people were often out and about, attending to certain errands they had no time for during their busy working week or on the Sabbath.

On this Sunday, just one day after the Germans had crossed our border, hardly anyone was out. The few people I saw were huddled together, talking quietly, as if they were concerned that someone might overhear them. I wondered what they could've been talking about so secretively but I had to hurry to avoid being late.

As I neared the gymnasium the sound of a police siren made me jump. I saw nothing wrong and kept walking toward the school. There must have been some normal crime going on, like someone stealing something from a store, or perhaps someone had a car accident and the police were rushing by to help, doing their job as usual.

What would it be like if the German army just suddenly rounded the corner and marched down the street, with hundreds and hundreds of soldiers in a line with their rifles and tanks rolling behind them, firing their guns in any direction they wanted?

The image of it sent chills up my spine, and I had to laugh at myself for picturing something so outrageous.

It wasn't going to happen like that. They'd never actually come all the way here to Amsterdam. No way. Enough of the fantasy already. I guess I'd been reading too many cheap adventure books. I reminded myself to get to gymnastics, and not to be late.

Thankfully, the next few hours gave me a chance to forget about all the terrible things I feared might happen. Exercising and participating in all the activities Mr. Koen laid out for us took me far away from any imagined world of impending doom. None of the boys spoke about what had occurred, especially because Mr. Koen kept us so busy, working us out on one apparatus after another until we were all exhausted.

I trudged home, tired from gymnastics and all the extra excitement surrounding my Bar Mitzvah, and especially from worrying about my father and all his fears. I wondered which of his theories would turn out to be true.

At the same time I was walking home, considering what I might eat for lunch, I had no idea that Queen Wilhelmina, the entire royal family, and most of the Dutch government officials were quickly packing up everything they could and preparing to flee to London before they were all captured and imprisoned by the Nazis.

Our house seemed normal when I returned. Mama was cooking in the kitchen. My sister was sewing, and my two brothers were playing chess in the living room. Papa came out of his room to greet me and then disappeared. Throughout the rest of the day, he stayed glued to the radio, waiting for the next piece of bad news. He didn't even eat dinner with the rest of us.

"Mama, please let me get Papa. He must be hungry."

"Stay here. He won't come. The news is getting worse every hour and he has no appetite."

"But he has to eat."

"Don't worry," Tinie said. "He'll eat when he's ready. For now, he has bigger things on his mind."

Daniel interrupted. "Can I please explain?"

Mama nodded. She seemed so worried.

I'd never seen her look so heavy in her heart.

"You see, Sal, the Dutch government has just officially departed from its historically neutral position and declared war on Germany."

Louis and Tinie sighed.

Mama closed her eyes and waited for Daniel to continue.

"Our armies have been fighting as best as they can on many fronts. In spite of a few small victories, it's becoming more and more clear that they will eventually crumble because of Germany's superior military. Too much fire power."

It was silent for a moment until my mother spoke. "Well said, Daniel. Okay, my dears, there's nothing we can do about this right now, so please finish your dinner."

A short time later, I tried to go to sleep but all I could imagine was a pair of big black boots pounding up the stairs to my bedroom. I tossed and turned, trying to erase the awful fantasy of these Germans taking me out of my bed in the middle of the night.

Before the sun had even risen on Monday, we were all shocked awake by the sounds of planes droning overhead, air raid sirens blaring, and what we thought must've been bombs exploding in the heart of Amsterdam.

No one I knew had any idea what a bomb sounded like when it went off, however with all those planes flying above us and the blasts and explosions that followed just a few heartbeats later, we all concluded, and correctly so, that our beloved hometown was being bombarded. It seemed like the bombs were dropping on another side of town but all we could do was hope we were right and that the terrible explosions would not happen any closer to us.

But they did. We ran downstairs into the basement of our building, hoping to escape from the effects of the bombing. As we sat together, huddled next to some old furniture and a rusty boiler, none of us said a word. The German air force was attacking key manufacturing ~~sights~~ sites on the outskirts of the city, and luckily none fell directly near our neighborhood.

A policeman startled us when he appeared in the doorway of the basement. "You can go upstairs now," he said matter-of-factly. "The bombs won't fall here."

"How can you be so sure?" said Louis. "You're a Dutch policeman, not a German bombardier!"

"Louis!" Mama said. "Sorry, Sir, we're all a bit nervous, you see."

"Right," the officer said. "Watch yourself, son."

He stared at Louis. His look was decidedly unfriendly and scared me half to death. He was supposed to be our protector, but I wasn't so sure in that moment.

"Are you sure it's safe?" Papa said.

"Yes, it's safe," the policeman said, "at least for now. But you never know, that could change overnight." As he left, he took one last glance at Louis and then at each of us, one by one. It was as if he was memorizing our faces in the candlelight.

Slowly, we marched back upstairs into our apartment.

"That policeman was creepy," Tinie said.

"He was just doing his job," said Mama.

"And what job does he do now, exactly?" said Daniel. "It seems like you can't be totally sure which side he's really on."

"He's on his own side," Papa said. "The side which protects him from the other."

"How can a Dutch policeman side with the Nazis? That's impossible."

"Go back to sleep, Sal."

"Your mother is right. And try not to dream too much."

The bombing continued for several hours, so by the time I was supposed to get up and go to school I was wide awake but thoroughly exhausted. My parents insisted that I stay home, and like any regular kid I didn't object. But I didn't feel the normal relief of skipping a day of school. I didn't want to leave our house and venture out into the streets. I was afraid of what I might see. I couldn't shake the image of those boots, those awful terrible big, black boots of the Nazi soldiers, marching through my city and up into my bedroom.

All day long, my family and I sat inside the apartment, pretending everything was normal when we knew it wasn't. We moved from room to room, peeking out of the windows, fearful of hearing the air raid sirens announcing another round of bombing. But no more came. Amsterdam, for the time being, had been spared more punishment.

"You see," Mama said, "it's not so bad today. Things are calm."

"For now they are but how long will that last?"

"Who can say? Come, let's eat dinner. Call your brothers and your sister."

We ate once again without our father, who stayed close to the radio in his room, hoping to catch a piece of positive news he could bring into the kitchen. But none came.

I went to sleep that night with the sounds of the German Luftwaffe flying overhead.

What were they doing? Hadn't they bombed us enough already?

I ran downstairs from my bedroom and found my parents sleeping.

"Papa! Wake up! Don't you hear the planes?"

"Come here and sit down," my mother said.

"No, I want to know what's going on, so tell me. Where are those planes going? Are they circling around to come after us here? Tell me, Papa!" I was so scared. Hearing myself ask these questions only intensified the feeling.

"I heard on the radio that they're on their way to the port of Rotterdam. They'll be bombing there all night if I know the Germans."

"But that's less than an hour's drive from Amsterdam."

"That's true, Sal, but I don't think they'll come here tonight."

"What makes you so sure?"

"I can't be sure. Honestly, I can't. But I'll bet they're finished with their bombing here in Amsterdam. Otherwise, they would've continued the other night."

"Go to sleep now, Sal. Nothing more will happen tonight. Try to sleep."

Over the next 24 hours, Rotterdam was unmercifully bombed by the German air force, and all in all 20,000 buildings were destroyed, thousands of people injured, and more than 1,000 people killed.

Two days later, General Henri Winkelman, commander-in-chief of the Netherlands Air and Sea forces, and the acting chief of the entire Dutch military, formally surrendered to the German Army. My father told us as we sat in the kitchen, drinking tea with our cake.

On May 16, 1940, just six days after my Bar Mitzvah, Nazi troops marched into Amsterdam. My father's long-held nightmare was finally coming true. The thunderous sound of boots pounding the cobblestones, which I had heard in my dreams a few nights before, was happening in real life right there in front of us.

Louis and Daniel and I slipped out of the apartment and made our way down the block to the corner. Hiding behind a few cars, we saw a large parade of soldiers and tanks moving along the main thoroughfare of our neighborhood. My heart was pounding a mile a minute in my chest. I couldn't take my eyes off those big men, dressed perfectly alike and marching with a supreme confidence, as if our streets were meant for them and their shiny boots.

I wanted to scream at them but I was too scared to make a sound. Louis looked so angry I was afraid he wouldn't be able to control himself. Daniel kept his hands over our mouths. After a few minutes, we crept back into our building, each of us shaking from what we had witnessed.

That morning I knew that life as I had known it up until then was effectively over for my entire family and me.

8

During the first weeks of the occupation in 1941, many people didn't notice the Germans on the streets of our city. They gave the illusion of blending in with the Dutch police. Throughout that first summer, nothing effectively changed in my daily life. My friends and I went about our normal activities, and aside from those awful nights of bombing, life at home seemed unaffected. My father remained moody, glued to the radio, and poring over the newspaper each evening when he returned from work.

I longed for the days when he played with us and was full of fun. But he had little reason to enjoy himself or celebrate anything anymore. Now it was work, radio, and the newspapers, bottling up all his attention and weighing down his emotions.

His non-Jewish friends who worked in government jobs had been forced to fill out a form with the German authorities, stating that they were not Jewish. Those who refused were fired from their positions, and so were all Jews. My father, tormented by the behavior he witnessed around him, struggled with his former colleagues and friends.

No one in the Netherlands could have possibly been prepared for the moral dilemmas they faced during this time. Even my elderly aunts and uncles had never experienced war. The Netherlands had been neutral during the First World War. In fact, our country had known peace for more than 100 years until the day German soldiers crossed our border. Our army had little time to prepare for serious fighting, and our citizens had no idea what it really meant to take sides in such a conflict.

One of my teachers, a non-Jew, couldn't bring herself to sign the decree, and she lost her job overnight. The next day in school I had a new teacher, a non-Jewish Dutch woman who had three children to feed. She couldn't afford to give up her employment, even if she had agreed with the protest. I'm sure she wasn't the only one who made that choice. Everyone had to take care of their family however they could.

Dutch society was divided in its sympathy for the worsening plight of the Jews. Many did whatever was necessary to preserve their way of life, because they didn't care, or they had a family to support, or they didn't believe the German occupation would last long.

However, quite a few Dutch people resisted the German decrees by helping their Jewish friends and colleagues.

By the time we rang in the new year of 1941, all Jews with civil service and government jobs had been fired. The only exceptions were those men who had been appointed to the newly formed Jewish Council. They were a mix of influential bankers, doctors, lawyers, and businessmen, used by the Germans to help them implement the first steps in their highly organized takeover of the Netherlands.

One night early in March, my father came home as we were having dinner. "I'm sorry, everyone, we have to go now," he said.

"Papa, what are you talking about?"

My father sat down to explain. "The Jewish Council contacted me recently about some new laws the Germans are making. Every Jew is required to register with the Jewish Council and obtain an identity card."

"What kind of nonsense is that?" said Louis. "We're all Jewish! Now we have to announce that to each other?" He laughed at the absurdity of it all.

"Please be quiet, Louis," my father said. "Listen to me, this is no joke. To make matters worse, Jews must pay one guilder for each of these…"

"What?" Louis said. "We have to pay to brand ourselves as Jews?"

"Yes, and the cards must be marked with a big "J" for *Jew*." He nodded to confirm it was true.

I don't know why I believed him. It sounded so crazy that we would have to carry these ID cards, and that we would have to pay for the privilege. "What happens if we don't have these ID cards?"

"Anyone who defies these orders risks imprisonment, at the very least."

"For not carrying a stupid card?" Louis said. "I should go to prison for that?"

"Louis, you're right. It's awful," Papa said. "I've toyed with the idea of not buying the ID cards but when I saw a few of my friends taken immediately to prison for doing that, I realized that we'd better comply so at least we have a chance of surviving."

"We have no choice," Mama said.

"Not if we want to live."

Dutch Jews were beginning to realize more and more that Hitler was determined to destroy the Jewish population of Europe. On the eighth anniversary of his rise to power in Germany, in a speech reported in all the Dutch newspapers, he repeated his threat to solve what he referred to as *die Judenfrage*, the "Jewish Problem."

After hearing that speech, my father came home from work every night claiming that it was just a matter of time before the Nazis eliminated everyone they deemed "undesirable."

"We must all watch our behavior. We mustn't give them any excuse to take us in to the police station, because once you go inside those buildings, you may never return."

"Oh, stop it, Papa. That's crazy."

"Papa, you're exaggerating." Tinie nearly laughed.

"I mean what I say," Papa said.

"You can't!" Louis said.

He slammed his fist on the table.

"You can't mean that!"

"Philip, stop now. You're frightening the children."

"Yes, maybe I am. But perhaps with good reason."

We all wanted to turn this into a game to make it all go away. I thought my father might be able to do it in that moment, all by himself, if he could just come up with a satisfying answer.

"I mean, just because I have an ID card doesn't mean they can arrest me just for doing nothing – for fooling around with my friends, right?"

"Of course not, Sal." My father was trying to soothe the situation.

"You see,?" said Mama. "Everything is not so bad. Don't listen to your father. He's just a little sensitive about this. He worries too much."

"Mama is right. Papa, you worry too much."

My father smiled and held his cup of wine in his hand for a long time before taking a sip. We all waited for him to respond, as if he could make it all better with one smile and a sip of magic wine.

"Hmm, maybe your mother's right, after all," he said. "So don't worry, at least for right now. Enjoy your dinner. Enjoy the chance for all of us to sit together at the table."

Just like the birthday wish I'd made, that we could all be together each year to celebrate these milestones. My father nodded to me and held up his glass of wine to make a toast.

"To family. When everything else fails, it's all we've got."

9

Although Hitler's army found many sympathizers in Holland, most Dutch people didn't share his philosophy of a superior race. Some of them protested openly against the Nazi regime, which led to decisive retaliation by the occupying soldiers.

On February 11, 1941, three Dutch Jews were arrested for the murder of a Dutch Nazi named Koot, and after their photos were displayed for everyone to see, no one ever heard from them again. Daniel knew two of the young men, and for days after they disappeared, he was deeply troubled by their fate. I couldn't help noticing how disturbed Daniel had become but I was afraid to ask him any questions.

Just a few days later, I had a scare of my own. Although money was tight during these times, my friends and I often managed to scrape together a few pennies to buy ice cream after school. In Amsterdam, the Koco ice cream parlor was famous for its delicious concoctions and the friendly owners who had emigrated years ago from Germany. Koco's was our favorite.

After the Germans occupied the city and started branding certain establishments as "Jewish," some of their patrons grew concerned for the owners' safety. They bought weapons for Ernst Cahn and his partner, just in case they should ever need to defend themselves in an emergency. One of those weapons was a 20-inch ammonia flask, installed on one of the parlor walls to deter any unwanted visitors.

On February 19, not long after my friends and I stopped by, a few German police officers entered Koco's and began harassing the owners. Although Ernst Cahn wasn't looking for trouble, some of his customers deeply resented the German soldiers and began pushing and shoving them. Amidst the chaos, someone sprayed the soldiers with the ammonia. Overcome by the fumes, they left in a hurry, however not before swearing revenge.

It didn't take them long. On February 22 and 23, SS troops aggressively raided the neighborhood where many Jews were living. Nearly 400 young Jewish men were randomly picked up off the streets in a series of roundups, called *razzias*.

They were beaten and taken to local jails for processing. For most of these older boys and young men, this was the start of a long and arduous imprisonment. Eventually, word spread that some of them were deported to a concentration camp in Buchenwald, Germany. Others were transported to Mauthhausen, where they were executed in the camp's stone quarry.

I heard about what happened at the ice cream parlor and made a point of avoiding it for a few weeks until the incident blew over. Antisemitism was spreading throughout the city, and the Nazis weren't the only ones promoting it. Dutch citizens were as guilty as anyone of abusing their fellow countrymen, and Jews were continuously surprised by the behavior of people they once considered friends.

My father's fears were coming true.

I was shocked one day at school when my mathematics teacher presented the following word problem: "If three Jews rob a bank, and each receives a piece of the loot proportionate to their ages, how much will each of them receive?"

I couldn't believe that my teacher could feel so strongly against Jews that he would make up such a terrible word problem to prove it. Some other students laughed and attempted to solve the problem. The other Jewish students and I sat silently, waiting for our teacher to continue.

When I saw my father at home that night and told him what happened, he sat silently and said nothing. Then, out of nowhere, he began to laugh.

"What a fool your mathematics teacher is, to stereotype Jewish people like that! Doesn't he realize that, for a Jew, robbing a bank is unnecessary?"

My father continued laughing, nearly spitting up his food.

"Papa, what's so funny?" I couldn't imagine how this disgusting joke could possibly be funny.

"You should remind your idiot teacher tomorrow that, according to Hitler, the Jews already own all the banks in Europe. Therefore, we have no need to rob any of them!"

10

Just when my friends and I thought it might be safe to return to Koco's, we heard that Ernst Cahn, the parlor's co-owner, had been executed by a German firing squad.

Throughout the night of March 3, 1941, I lay awake, wondering how such a thing could happen. Mr. Cahn was such a nice man. Why would the Germans kill him?

It was the first time I ever thought about anyone killing another person. I understood that people die, from sickness or old age, or even in some tragic way, like a car accident. But I'd never considered what it meant for one human being to kill another, especially when there was no apparent reason, at least one I could relate to. On top of that, it was someone I knew.

I tossed and turned in my bed, trying to make sense of what the Nazis had done. If they could arrest Ernst Cahn and kill him so easily, without even putting him on trial, who else could they just pick up and shoot whenever they felt like it? What if I had been in Koco's when the Nazis came and took Mr. Cahn away? Could they have taken me with him?

I lay in my bed, terrified that anyone in my family could be taken away at any time and executed. I finally fell asleep but it didn't last long. The news of Ernst Cahn's murder wouldn't let me rest. I sat up, consumed by thoughts of the killing.

What does it feel like to have a bullet go through your skin?

What does it feel like when it first penetrates your flesh?

Does it hurt? It must hurt a lot.

When a bullet is fired, it's noisy. There's a big bang, just like in the movies. I've heard that on the street. It's loud and quick, and then it's suddenly quiet again, as if nothing happened.

I couldn't stop tormenting myself with morbid fantasies.

If I am shot, what will it feel like?

When the bullet goes through my skin, will it crunch my bones?

Will it explode into my guts?

Will I feel the most excruciating pain that's even possible?

How long will it last before I just fall over and die?

Where will the bullet enter my body? Does the pain depend on that?

Will my blood spurt all over my shirt?

Will I sink to my knees, collapse onto my back, and die immediately?

Will the bullet stagger me for a moment?

If I'm shot in the leg and my organs are okay, will it feel like I've been kicked in the shins by someone with a steel-toed boot?

Will I scream in pain but I won't die?

What then? Will anyone help me? Will I limp away by myself? Will anyone help me? Will I be left alone to die in the street, lying in my own blood, like a lousy gangster?

Will the Germans shoot me again without killing me and take me away to die in one of their prisons?

I exhausted myself considering the possibilities and fell asleep.

When I awoke, I discovered my nightmares had just begun.

11

"Mama, could we go to the cinema this weekend for my birthday? Frank says they're showing a new *Tarzan* movie from America and I'd like to see it."

"Sal, you know we can't do that. The new law prohibits us from going to the cinema or the theaters."

"No movies? Since when?"

"Just this week. Look at this."

She handed me *Het Joodsche Weekblad*, a new weekly newspaper specifically targeted for Jewish readers. The Germans had recently organized it so we wouldn't miss the news about all the new restrictions being placed on us.

"How can they do that? It's bad enough we can't even go to a restaurant on my birthday. Now we can't even see a movie?" I tossed the newspaper onto the table and headed out of the kitchen. It was hard to believe a whole year had passed since the German invasion.

"Sal, wait. There must be something else we can do together. How about the zoo?"

"Mama, please. Besides the fact that I'm too old for a silly zoo, according to that stupid paper it's now forbidden for Jews to go there. And even if we could, it would be a long walk."

My mother looked at me quizzically.

"Mama, we can't ride the trams anymore. No Jews allowed. Wherever we're still allowed to go, we have to walk!"

We abandoned making plans for doing anything special for my birthday. We celebrated quietly at home with the family and my friend, Frank. There were bigger and more important things happening all around us, and now we didn't need our father to remind us.

During that spring and summer, the Germans instituted a series of rules and regulations meant to cut all of us off from the rest of Dutch society. Slowly but surely, the Nazis were making ordinary life impossible for the Jews of Amsterdam.

We were forbidden to drive cars, even our own. No public transportation. If any Jew was caught hopping on a tram, they could be arrested. German soldiers routinely boarded the trams and checked people's papers. If they discovered a "J" on your ID card, you could disappear without a word.

When the temperatures warmed up and summer was in full swing, the Germans closed all public swimming pools to Jews. We were forbidden from using any park facilities – no boating, no tennis, no football – nothing. Jews were no longer allowed in Vondelpark, where Louis and I had once raced our bicycles en route to Eindhoven.

I couldn't go far from my own neighborhood. I couldn't even roam the streets I'd known my entire life. Jews were forbidden to ride their bicycles. Jewish boys and girls were not allowed to play outside anymore. We were quickly becoming prisoners in our own homes.

12

As 1941 blended into 1942, we tried our best to continue living normally. Because of all the laws controlling how we moved around the city, we were forced to adjust our schedules to account for the extra time it took to walk everywhere. We weren't alone. The new restrictions were affecting thousands of Jews in Amsterdam.

Everywhere we went we encountered the same signs: JEWS PROHIBITED.

Somehow, we had to persevere and adapt. No one liked these restrictions, of course, but we knew we had to accept our fate, at least for the time being, until the Germans could eventually be driven out of our country by British and American armies.

I couldn't have my hair cut any longer by Mr. Kleiman, my favorite barber, because a new law stated that Jews could not go to non-Jewish barbers. Reluctantly, I went to the only Jewish barber in my neighborhood, Mr. Vanderpol, who had butchered my hair a few years ago, and still insisted on cutting it shorter than I preferred. Even though Mr. Kleiman felt bad that he couldn't cut my hair, he said it would be too risky because if he was caught cutting a Jew's hair he could get into a lot of trouble. I understood his predicament but I still felt worse about mine. I was the one stuck with a lousy haircut.

Since I was no longer able to spend any time with my non-Jewish friends, they also couldn't tease me for having such a rotten-looking cut. I came to know my Jewish schoolmates better and spent more time with them. But our options for adventure were disappearing. After school, we often accompanied our mothers to help them with their shopping. Everything had to be done between the hours of three and five in the afternoon, and Jews could only buy food and other necessities from Jewish shops.

The rules didn't stop there. On our way to and from home, we were forced to pay strict attention to where we walked. According to German law, Jews were barred from the sunny side of the street.

I hated this law so badly. The other restrictions were horrible enough. But it was as if the Nazis were making themselves into gods who could dictate our exposure to nature. To the sun! How could anyone dare to control the sun?

Some Jews made the mistake of trying to have it their own way. One day, I saw a group of high school kids I knew, walking and playing on the sunny side of the street. It wasn't long before they were rounded up and taken away. I never saw them again.

From that time on, I decided to obey the laws. I had no desire to disappear. I missed the sunshine but I would miss my family much, much more.

In the evenings, when the sun had set for everyone, Jews and non-Jews alike, we had to be inside our homes by 8 p.m. in accordance with the curfew. Any Jew caught outside after that time risked arrest, or worse, a trip to one of the German camps. From what we heard, no one ever came back from one of them.

We adapted as best as we could, while we were methodically stripped of what had once been our natural rights as citizens of our country. Month by month, and year by year, the Germans set in place the mechanisms that enabled them to efficiently deport thousands of people at a time.

Although Jews were continuously being arrested, and many vanished never to be seen again, most of us couldn't imagine the horrible extent of the Nazi's secret plan. We had no idea of the terrible fate in store for us in the concentration camps in our country and eastern Europe.

Most of us thought it couldn't get much worse, and if we could just hang on a little longer, the war would be over and life as we had known it would be restored.

I comforted myself with that thought every single day.

Even when my brother Louis and I were forced to go to an all-Jewish school in East Amsterdam, neither of us thought it would be permanent.

So it came as quite a shock in the first week of May 1942 when it was declared that all Jews would have to wear a yellow Star of David, displayed prominently on our outer clothing. This new law shocked all of us. From that day on, wherever we went in the city, anyone and everyone would see us marked as Jews – as if something were wrong with us, as if we were an inferior people. And to add insult to injury, we had to pay for these yellow stars ourselves.

One Jew equals one guilder. One guilder equals one life.

It wasn't so long ago that we had been ordered to carry ID cards, officially registering ourselves as Jews. At the time we thought that was an awful thing to be forced to do. But those cards didn't seem so bad in retrospect, compared to wearing a bright yellow badge on our outer clothing, advertising our identity to the entire world.

A few days later, it was time to celebrate my 15th birthday. My family decided we would go to the theater for a matinee performance. By that time, the great Dutch national theater, which used to be called the Hollandsche Schouwburg, had been renamed the Joodsche Schouwburg, or Jewish Theater. It was now the only place in Amsterdam where Jewish artists – musicians, actors, and so on – were permitted to work, and the only theater Jews were allowed to attend.

Before leaving our apartment, we made sure that each of us were wearing our yellow stars, and that they were easily visible for any German policeman to see. As we walked through the streets of Amsterdam, we felt terribly conspicuous yet proud of who we were, especially my nervous father.

When we returned home a few hours later, we all gathered in the kitchen to light the candles on my birthday cake. With food shortages taking effect, it had been difficult for my mother to scrounge up the ingredients but she managed, even though she had to place used candles on top of the cake.

"Sal, you're getting bigger every year."

"What do you mean, Mama? He's not so big!"

"Yeah, he's a squirt, actually." Louis poked me in the ribs.

"Oh, stop it, all of you. He's a baby-face, my beautiful little brother." Tinie wrapped her arms around me. Luckily, this was a family affair, and all this corny behavior was behind closed doors.

"Quiet now, all of you," Mama said, "it's time to sing."

"Can we hurry, please?" said Papa. "The news is coming on the radio."

With 15 candles burning, I wished for the same thing I did every year, that I would celebrate more birthdays with my family, as always. Little did I know, as I blew out all the candles, that my 15th birthday would be the last event we would ever celebrate together.

13

"Sal, you must concentrate."

Mr. Lentz, my cello teacher, was trying to help but I was having trouble concentrating as we sat in the living room of our apartment one afternoon after school.

Ever since I began taking lessons with him when I was eight years old, they had been at his apartment. But since the law went into effect banning Jews from setting foot inside non-Jews' houses, Mr. Lentz came to our apartment. With neighbors gossiping more and more, he was risking his life by coming to our place. Since he wasn't Jewish, Mr. Lentz might be viewed as a sympathizer, which could have jeopardized his standing in the community. It wasn't uncommon for antisemitic neighbors, those sympathetic to the Nazis, to report to the police what they considered unacceptable behavior.

"I've known you a long time," Mr. Lentz said. "Concentration has never been difficult for you. What's troubling you today?"

I continued playing, drawing the bow across my cello.

"Please, you're making the same mistake, over and over." Mr. Lentz took my arm gently and moved the bow away from the cello. "Stop now."

"I'm sorry. I'm trying but I can't help it. My head is not really here. It's everything. It's all these laws and restrictions. I can't stand it. I try to ignore it and think it will go away but my father is getting crazy, screaming about how our lives will be over soon, that any day we'll go fry in a big oven in Poland. I'm afraid when he talks like that, Mr. Lentz. It's crazy and terrible, I'm sorry. I can't concentrate right now."

"I don't know what to say."

"I know. How could you? I'm sorry. I know this isn't nice for you and I'm wasting your time but I can't help it." Mr. Lentz placed the bow in the cello case.

"No bicycles, Mr. Lentz. No playing in the park. I have to go to a different school. I can't go to Frank's house after eight o'clock. I can't go to the cinema. I can't go anywhere!"

"Sal, I am sorry. We're living in some atrocious dream. It's not just you Jews who are affected by these outrageous rules. I have many Jewish friends and I can't visit them anymore like I used to. Look at us. You can't come into my house for a lesson. My Jewish friends can't come for a coffee, either. It's no good for any of us."

"That's for sure, Mr. Lentz."

"Listen. We must make the best of this impossible situation. It can't last much longer. You'll see. It'll be over soon, once the British and the Americans finally fight together against the Germans. You will see, it will end soon."

I nodded.

"For now, let's have some fun. I want to ask you a favor. I don't think I can ask your father. It might upset him too much."

"It doesn't take much these days."

"Exactly. So, I would like to attend the Jewish orchestra recital at the Jewish Theater that is being held there tonight."

"Mr. Lentz!"

I was surprised at his apparent indifference to the regulations. "Only Jews can attend performances there. Only Jews can perform, and only Jews can go see them. What are you proposing? You could get in big trouble. Please don't do such a thing."

"Sal, please pay attention. I desperately want to attend the concert tonight. It would mean a great deal to me. It's a once-in-a-lifetime performance by Amsterdam's greatest Jewish musical artists, led by the legendary conductor, Albert van Raalte, who is also a Jew of course."

"It should be a great concert, you're right."

"Yes, I know, and I would like to borrow, if I may, your yellow Star of David so I can attend the performance tonight."

"Oh my God, what a request. I never imagined anyone asking me for my star."

"Please, may I borrow it?"

"I don't know."

What if I gave Mr. Lentz my yellow star? If he were caught wearing it, impersonating a Jew no less. He could get into terrible trouble. I wouldn't have my star to wear so I'd be stuck inside the house forever. How would I get a replacement?

"Suppose I do give it to you. Will you be sure to get it back to me right after the concert? My mother will have to sew it back onto my jacket. I need it to go to school in the morning."

"Of course I will. I give you my word."

"Okay then, I guess I can give it to you. But Mr. Lentz, why would you want to pretend to be a Jew?"

Mr. Lentz smiled. "That's easy, Sal. For the music."

14

It wasn't long before the teachers in our Jews-only school began disappearing. The German Police, known as the *Grüne Polizei*, or green police from the color of their uniforms, were taking away so many people that whenever they came to our school, no one knew if they were looking for a teacher or about to take away a student.

Each time we were tipped off by the principal or heard the police approaching, we ran to hide. The sound of their jackboots clacking their heels up the stairs and down the hallway became mixed with the mad shuffling of the children, scrambling to vacate classrooms before the police arrived. Half our minds were consumed by fear, and the other half couldn't believe it was true. It was like we were caught in a thrilling game, and we were the major characters. But as the boots came closer, we grew terrified.

My classroom looked out on a courtyard that included a small playground surrounded by three other buildings. The outdoor space was accessible by a single door or through a lower set of four windows.

One morning, when we were beginning a science test, everyone stopped when we heard the familiar sound of those heavy boots. Twenty-seven children looked up in unison, dropped their pencils, and in one sweeping motion, we vacated our desks, grabbed our jackets from the backs of our chairs, and scrambled for the exits.

"Move it!" our teacher said. "Let's go now, everyone!"

We screamed in fear.

"No time to be scared now!"

My cousin, Marcus, was yelling at us to leave.

By this time it was a well-choreographed routine. The physically bigger students ran out through the door, and those of us who were small enough shimmied through the windows and out into the courtyard. It all happened extremely fast.

The chase was on.

I never looked back, even as I heard the shouting come dangerously close. I ran and hurdled the low wall separating the school from an apartment building, and I didn't stop there. The police were yelling at us. I didn't know whether they were trying to frighten us or if they were serious about catching us. I had no intention of slowing down enough to find out.

Marcus and I ran as fast as we could, up the inside stairs of the building, down the hallway of the second floor, and back down a rear set of stairs and into another courtyard. Through the next building, we saw some small backyards, each with its own private doorway.

"You sure, Marcus?"

"No choice."

Marcus was confident. He was a good athlete and physically fearless. He always had been, ever since we were little boys.

Neither of us hesitated We selected the only open door available and ran straight through it into someone's apartment. I had no idea whose house we were invading. We ran right through their living room, paying no attention to the screaming woman folding clothes into a laundry basket. We continued out her kitchen door, through a small alleyway, and across two streets, dodging city traffic to finally escape the police by entering my cousin's apartment. Once we were safely inside his living room and the front door was shut, we waited for the sound of the police knocking loudly, demanding that we open the door.

"Sal, what are we going to do when they get here?"

"I don't know. Who says they're going to find us?"

"They'll find us. Believe me, they find everybody."

"Well, maybe not this time."

"Yeah, maybe not. If we're lucky."

"We must be lucky. We have to be."

"They'll be here any minute."

Marcus groaned. We both dreaded what was to come. We had no idea what we would do in that moment but it never happened. The sounds we feared never came. The police must have lost us while we ran through that stranger's house. By the time Marcus and I felt our heart rates return to normal, we realized we were out of danger, at least for the time being.

My uncle returned home a few hours later and called my father to pick me up, hopefully to return safely to our home. I was still exhilarated by the police chase, however my father was deeply disturbed. We walked home in silence, wearing our yellow badges for everyone to see.

15

"It's happening." Papa was speaking to us a few months later as we gathered around the kitchen table on a muggy July evening. "What we've been fearing all along but thought unimaginable is now happening."

"What's happening that we don't already know; that we can't see with our own eyes?"

"You see, Mama," said Louis, "your little boy is growing up."

"Shut up," said Daniel. "Listen to your father."

"Please, boys, no fighting. Not now." Papa closed his eyes for a moment as if he didn't want to continue but he knew he must. "The Germans are collecting all Jews, one by one, family by family. They come in the night, when it's dark and quiet, or early in the morning, before the curfew is lifted, while no one is allowed outside."

"Without any warning?"

"Yes, Rachel. No warning. It's impossible to resist. They take whoever they want."

Daniel started to say something.

"If you resist, you will be shot and killed."

Daniel bit his lip and kept quiet.

"What's the point of all this?" asked Louis.

"Yeah, Papa, how do you know so much?" I asked, hoping he really didn't know anything.

"Sal, you don't need to hear any more," said Mama.

"Mama, I need to know!"

"Okay, we all must understand the situation. The Nazis are rounding up more and more Jews every night and taking them away to the collection center. I know people who have escaped, however that's not easy to do, and it's pure luck they're still alive."

"Papa, you're scaring me. You're scaring all of us."

"My dear boy, I'm sorry." My father looked at all of us, one by one. "There is a way we can avoid this. There is a way we can die in dignity."

We sat quietly. We weren't sure we had heard him correctly.

"Papa, what are you saying?"

"I'm saying there is another way."

"Are you speaking of suicide?"

"You want us to kill ourselves?" Daniel was screaming.

"Daniel! Don't raise your voice to your father."

"Listen to me," Papa said. "I beg you. Listen to me."

"Philip, this is crazy."

"Rachel, let me speak. Let me finish, please."

We waited for him to continue, as if he might have a magic answer.

"I am deeply afraid of what could happen to all of us. They are monsters! If we do this, we can create a dignified death in the face of the Nazis. We can have one small piece of control over our own destiny."

"I'll never do that. I will fight them," Daniel said.

"You will fight them?" asked Papa.

"Yes, I will."

He sounded so sure of himself, and being much older than me, and someone I'd looked up to my entire life, I wanted to believe him.

"What will you fight them with, your ideas?"

"I don't know, but I will fight."

"Me too," Louis said. "I'll fight until the death. I won't give them the pleasure of seeing one more dead Jew without trying myself to make one dead Nazi."

"Enough." Papa stood up. "I'm sorry everyone. I just thought..." He never finished. Papa left the kitchen and shut the bedroom door behind him.

"Can you believe we just heard this?" I asked.

"Oh my God, I'm worried about Papa," said Tinie.

"Me too," Mama said. "I must go to your father."

Daniel, Tinie, Louis, and I were left in the kitchen, staring at the table or each other. None of us could say anything. We'd all noticed our father sinking deeper and deeper into depression as more and more Jews disappeared. Many of his friends had lost their jobs. Their bank accounts were closed or blocked.

The Germans were telling everyone that Jews were being sent to work in Germany. Anyone who refused would be sent to Mauthausen concentration camp. It wasn't long before people in the resistance realized how insidious the Nazis' plans really were.

My father didn't know what to do. Although he was educated and well informed, like many other Dutch Jews he felt powerless when it came to fighting the Nazis. What could one man do? He was imagining everything possible to keep our family safe.

I broke the silence around the table. "Papa used to say, 'Knowledge is power.'"

"Yeah?" Louis said. "Even knowing what the Germans will do doesn't mean any of us has the power to stop them."

"You mean, they can come in the middle of the night and take one of us?"

"Yes, whenever they want, wherever they want," said Daniel. "It's no big secret."

"So, we're just sitting here, waiting for them to come get us?" Tinie said.

"Something like that."

"I won't commit suicide," Tinie said, "but I won't just sit here, either."

"What will you do?"

"I don't know."

Mama returned and sent us to bed, kissing each of us as we left the kitchen. I paused at the bottom of the steps before going upstairs to my room and heard her muttering to herself as she picked up our glasses from the table and brought them to the sink. "There's every reason to be afraid," she said.

She was right. Everything my father had feared had come true, and much faster than imagined. In the coming days, the Germans surprised Amsterdam's Jews with another *razzia* – a swift, and violent round-up – indiscriminately arresting Jewish men at gunpoint in the street.

Some of our neighbors vanished without warning. It was like the Germans had a big, powerful eraser and could just remove people from a photo with a swipe across the paper.

Each morning we left our house and we didn't know if we would return. Every night I went to sleep, I didn't know if I would be awoken by the sound of black boots coming to get us.

Just weeks after we sat together in the kitchen, speaking about the possibility of such a thing happening to one of us, Daniel was caught on his way home from work. Not a word to tell us what happened.

One day, he came home from work as usual, and the next day, he didn't.

None of us ever heard from Daniel.

When Louis turned 16, he was ordered to report to German headquarters. With no plan for any type of escape and no idea where he might go, he reported as instructed. My parents feared the worst yet hoped for the best. Maybe the German quota for the night would be filled. Maybe there would be no more space to keep Louis.

But Louis never came home.

Not long after he disappeared, Tinie had to enter the hospital for a minor knee operation. I saw her briefly the day after her surgery. Before she was fully healed, she was taken from her hospital bed and shipped God knows where. Again, we heard nothing.

Tinie was gone.

That night in the kitchen turned out to be our last together.

My father grew silent and kept more and more to himself. It was as if he lost more of his voice with each disappearing child.

57

"Take me, instead."

I heard him moaning over and over in his bedroom. Pieces of his soul had been removed, one at a time. I stopped asking questions because I knew he had no answers.

I had lost my two brothers and my dear sister. The house became unbearably empty. Every day I woke up dreading the inevitable. Until it happened.

The *Joodse Raad*, a Jewish Council organized by the Nazis and forced to cooperate with the German authorities, ordered my father to report to the old Jewish Theater, where they assembled Jews to deport them to the camps. He barely had a word to say when he left the house one evening after dinner, with one small suitcase in his hand.

He held my head in his hands and stared into my face for what he must have known might be the last time. I tried to fill up my visual memory with this picture of my father, as if I could create a photograph of him inside myself, one that nothing could erase.

"Take care of your mother."

And then he was gone.

16

I was 15 years old in the summer of 1942, no longer a boy who used to see the world as his playground. There were no innocent children left in Amsterdam. The Germans had made sure of that. Since they'd invaded two years ago, just before my Bar Mitzvah, things had become progressively worse.

We tried to get by, one day at a time. But one by one, they were all gone – Daniel, Louis, Tinie, and now Papa – all gone without a trace.

How could this be? Where were they? Would I ever see them again?

This was like a bad dream. I couldn't believe all of this had happened.

Daniel was my tall, strong, smart hero of a brother. Louis, while always teasing me, was my best friend and playmate. Tinie was the warmest, sweetest big sister a boy could ever want. My father had always been so optimistic and supportive, until the Nazi invasion broke him and turned him into a small and fearful man. But I still loved him!

All of them now gone. It was just Mama, my old aunt and me. When would our turn come? And how?

Every day we heard reports of people disappearing or being shot on the spot. With the Nazis, bad luck was random. They killed, not only according to a schedule but whenever and wherever they felt like it.

17

"Sal, that was beautiful." My mother was trying to be nice after I finished an étude on my cello.

I shrugged.

"Come back and play more, won't you?"

I went to the window of our sitting room and pulled back the shade a tiny bit. "It looks normal out there. Some clouds, some rain, nothing unusual."

"Come play more. I love listening to you."

"Maybe today they'll be back."

"Look, you've put her sweetly to sleep." Mama pointed to Aunt Rose.

"Yeah, I'm really good at that."

"A nice Beethoven nap for your lovely old aunt."

My father's aunt slept comfortably in her easy chair. She was alone now that her children and grandchildren had disappeared. There was no one left to take care of her, so my mother had invited her to live with us. Most of the time, she sat in the living room and knitted, and napped.

Every day I woke up, I thought it might be the day that Daniel or Louis or Tinie would return home. Or my father. If just one of them showed up, it had to mean the others were not far behind. I carried this dream with me all day, every day.

"Sal, play."

Practice, practice, practice – that's all I had heard since I was eight years old. Both of my parents always encouraged me to play the cello but it was my mother, and Mr. Lentz, who had pushed me to practice every day.

Now, I was trying to force myself to learn a new étude when it was the furthest thing from my mind. I was trying to please my mother, who needed any diversion I could provide to take her mind off our terrible situation. We were both trying to maintain our belief that the war would soon be over, and that everyone would return home.

Even though they'd been gone for months already, we had no idea where they were. Everyone we knew offered up ideas. They might still be in the Westerbork transit camp in the Netherlands. They might be in a work camp in Germany. They might have been sent on one of the weekly trains to the concentration camps in Auschwitz, far away in Poland. Or maybe they were in hiding somewhere inside the Netherlands.

I wondered if Daniel was working with the Dutch resistance. Ever since that night at the kitchen table when he said nothing and sat still, biting his lip, listening to our father's crazy idea of family suicide, I wondered about the possibility of Daniel having a secret life, so secret that he wasn't even allowed to tell his own family.

Daniel had spoken so strongly about fighting the Nazis, as if he might have already done so in some shape or form. I thought he might've gone underground and was staying there, somewhere inside the country. Whether it was Amsterdam or some other place, I had no idea but I liked the notion of my big brother secretly fighting the Nazis and returning home a hero.

"Sal, what are you waiting for?" Mama interrupted my romantic ideas about Daniel and the resistance fighters. I wanted to ask her about where Daniel might be, and Louis, and Tinie, and of course my father but she and I had some an unwritten agreement that we wouldn't discuss such matters openly, as if talking about them might jinx the luck they would need to return home safe and sound. Although I knew it was a ridiculous superstition, I had to respect it.

Mama was suffering terribly, having possibly lost her husband and three of her children. The radio reports from London talked about Jews being gassed in concentration camps, and there was a chance that my brothers, my sister, and my father could be among the thousands of people Hitler was sending to those camps. Perhaps if we didn't talk about it, it simply wouldn't happen. I slid my bow across the strings, trying to create some noise to take my mind away from the things I couldn't comprehend. "There, you hear that, Mama?" I hoped she would be pleased. "It's the étude you like."

She turned her head in my direction, but her eyes were looking straight through me, staring someplace else. I had never seen her face like that before and it frightened me. "Mama? What is it?" I rested the bow over my leg. Mama was concentrating on another sound. Suddenly, her head snapped toward the window, and she froze, seemingly unable to stand up and move. She motioned for me to be quiet. Instead of standing up to go to the window, she crawled across the floor and opened the window a crack for me to listen.

I could hear soldiers marching, lots of them, their heels clicking on the wet pavement like a perfect machine, advancing up our street. Crouching down on my knees, I could hear their unmistakable voices barking out commands in loud, coarse German. It was the sound every Jew in Amsterdam dreaded hearing, especially marching toward their apartment building. It could only mean one thing, and we both knew it. Our eyes met, digesting what was about to happen.

"Sal, go upstairs right now. Go and hide."

I was paralyzed with fear and wasn't ready to leave my mother. My body tensed up, as if to attack but I knew that was a futile idea to imagine, even for a second. What could I possibly do against an entire squadron of German soldiers?

"Go!"

I could trick them. For a second, I thought I could seal the front door so the Germans would think the house had been cleared out. We could hide in our home until the war ended and my father, brothers, and sister all returned. "Mama, I can't."

"You must."

"I can't leave you."

"Sal, go upstairs right now and hide."

"We can both hide. Come on." I pleaded with her not to separate.

"No, Sal, I can't. I can't do that."

"Mama, please!"

"Your Aunt Rose. What shall I do with her?"

We both knew there was no suitable answer.

"The Nazis know. Believe me, they know we are here."

My mother tugged on my arm, pulling me away from the window. I glanced outside. Five trucks filled with German SS soldiers and the Dutch black police had screeched to a halt outside our building.

My chest was pounding faster and faster. The hammering of the boots and the menacing voices became louder. I couldn't breathe. I grabbed my mother's hand. The boots were coming closer, those terrible black boots which I could never shake out of my mind. The soldiers' voices grew louder as they entered our building.

There was only one family living in the ground-floor apartment, and they weren't Jewish. The other family on the second floor had disappeared weeks ago, in the middle of the night.

"Sal, go."

Mama took my hand and forcefully separated it from hers. In mere minutes, the police would march up the stairs and pound on our door. She kissed my hand. My mind froze. She motioned sharply toward the stairs. "Now." A look of anger and pain and love and fear washed over her face all at once. "Go."

I knew this was my final chance. My mother kissed my hand and touched me on my cheek. I stared at her for another second, taking a photo of her face for safekeeping in my mind. I didn't know how I could leave her there.

We heard soldiers slamming doors on the ground floor. Mama pointed down at my shoes. I removed them and looked back at her, unsure if I could make myself get up.

"Go."

We heard the police yelling at the foot of our stairs. I was too scared to feel anything as the boots started slamming up the steps. I darted past my mother in my stocking feet, carrying a shoe in each hand. I ran out of our living room as quietly as I could and tiptoed up to the fourth floor. As I opened the door to my bedroom, I heard the vicious pounding of the Nazi soldiers, ready to invade our apartment.

Upstairs, I found the only hiding place I could, behind the door in a curved niche in the wall where I usually hung my jacket. As I flattened myself into the hollow corner, I pulled the door open so that it closed me into my hiding place. I stood there shaking, behind the door, not knowing what would happen next.

18

My mind was racing so fast I don't think I heard the noise downstairs. Were they hurting my mother and my aunt? What would they do when they came upstairs? If I got caught, standing there behind the door, would they just shoot me right there on the spot?

I could hardly breathe.

Doors opened and shut. I couldn't tell what was happening one floor below. I never heard any voices and didn't know what that meant. No gunshots. No idea how many men were there.

I could hardly breathe.

All I felt was sweat gathering on my hand holding the inside of the doorknob. I was afraid I would lose my grip and the door would come free. I didn't know what to do. How could I dry off my hand and hold the door against me? What if that made noise?

I felt something move by my foot. I looked down but the light was dim behind the door. I felt it again.

A mouse!

I nearly jumped. I was so scared my feet wouldn't budge. I had to stay still and let the mouse move over my foot.

What was a mouse doing there? How could I get rid of it? Would it squeak? It could go anywhere it wanted, and when the Nazis came upstairs, they could find the mouse and trace it to me and kill both of us. One big black boot slamming down on that mouse to kill it immediately. Then, one bullet into my head would finish me off. All it would take was a single German soldier to commit two acts of murder.

I could hardly breathe.

It sounded like three or four men were congregating at the bottom of the stairs, grunting and calling to each other and laughing. They were laughing with each other as if there was something funny going on.

The mouse moved away from my foot but I couldn't tell where it was. Was the mouse scared like me, frozen still, unable to move, trying not to breathe and make any noise?

Two sets of footsteps began to climb the stairs. They stopped halfway up. "Come on, let's go! No one is here."

"Wait!"

I could hardly breathe.

The other one advanced up the stairs. He stopped at the doorway to my bedroom, inches from where I stood behind the door. I thought my head would just blow off from fear. I was sure he would hear me breathing. I closed my eyes to try and think of something calm.

The soldier on the stairs said something and the man next to me started laughing again. He laughed pretty hard, as if it was a good joke. A joke. They both laughed and then the hallway exploded.

A gunshot!

My ears were ringing. I don't know how I didn't scream but I didn't, or maybe I did and they didn't hear me over the blast.

One of the Nazis had fired a gun. They laughed loudly and then they were gone. All I could hear through the pounding in my head was the sound of their boots and their laughter, descending down the stairs.

For what felt like an eternity, I didn't move from my secret spot behind the door. My hand gripped the doorknob. I was frozen, afraid to breathe because it might be too loud.

What did they shoot?

I didn't know if I wanted to know but I had an idea. I heard the front door slam shut and then nothing. I waited. I waited a long time.

Maybe it was just five minutes. Maybe it was much longer, until I thought it was finally safe to move.

I slowly pushed the door open and looked around. It was my room, yet it didn't look the same anymore. Black boots and gunshots had changed it in an instant. Then I saw the mouse, in pieces, exploded by a bullet. Bloody chunks were stuck onto the wall.

Only a real monster could've done that. And only his friends would've laughed.

Through a small window, I looked down four flights onto the street. I was shocked to see my mother and my old aunt, each carrying a single suitcase, surrounded by German soldiers. Aunt Rose was struggling with the weight of the suitcase, but the police couldn't have cared less. They pushed her forward, nearly knocking her to the ground. My mother held her upright, and one of the soldiers crudely prodded them forward with his nightstick.

I wanted to yell out to them. I wanted to save them. All I could do was watch as they were marched away down the street and into the back of an enormous truck. They joined other Jews from adjacent buildings, and the soldiers squeezed in as many as they could before shutting the back gate of the vehicle.

My mother never looked back toward our building. That would have alerted the soldiers' attention to the possibility of someone else still being there. I wished more than anything that she would have turned back for just a second, that she would've looked up at me staring down from the window. She could have smiled, letting me know that everything would be okay. I knew full well that she wouldn't risk my safety. I just had to imagine her look of comfort and love.

"Don't worry, Sal. I'll be back soon," she would've said. "We'll all be back soon, together again, just like before."

A boy could wish.

After lingering a while at the window, I realized I had to go. I went downstairs to the living room. Everything was in order. They hadn't taken any possessions, or at least I didn't notice anything missing. I had heard from my father that after the Germans took people away from their homes, others would return to take whatever they wanted.

I had no idea when that might be. I wasn't going to stick around long enough to find out.

I stood perfectly still and closed my eyes. I could see my family gathered in the living room. As I stepped toward the kitchen, I could hear my brothers and sister and my parents singing to me on my birthdays.

It had been almost three years since the Germans invaded, three years since my Bar Mitzvah day, when I had supposedly become a man. But I didn't feel manly in that moment, standing alone inside our empty apartment. I felt terribly small and powerless. After all the fear I felt upstairs hiding behind the door, I felt angry. Who were these German devils, taking my family away and taking over our country?

How could this happen? Where was God in all of this? Where was justice? What were we praying for when we prayed for peace? What was the point?

I grabbed my cello, threw it on the floor, and kicked it spinning across the room. I'd never felt such anger. I jumped up and came down hard on the cello with both my feet, smashing it into a splintered pile of wood and strings.

I wanted to scream but my throat was completely dry and choked. My chest was heaving. I kicked my cello one last time. Still in a rage, I ran downstairs and out into an empty street. I stood there alone, with no idea of what to do next.

19

I stood in the street for a long time. When it began to get dark, signaling that our curfew would soon be in effect, I began to walk.

I soon found myself on the doorstep of my cousin's house. I couldn't remember how I got there but hoped I had found a safe place to rest before figuring out what to do next.

My cousin was Jewish, but she was married to Bram, a Christian, so I had no idea if either of them were still in Amsterdam. Even though we hadn't had any contact for quite some time, I hoped at least one of them would be there to help me. I didn't know where else to go.

There were no lights on inside the house. I thought it might be abandoned, that Bram and my cousin had been taken away in the police raids. I took a chance and rang the doorbell. I waited for a response, As I feared, nothing happened.

Just as I was about to walk away, I heard a small noise inside the house. Luckily, for the time being at least, Bram had hidden himself well. As he pulled me inside, his eyes darted up and down the street, surveying the area for potential trouble. Anyone found on the street after curfew could be arrested or shot on the spot.

I was so shocked when Bram grabbed me, I almost fainted. He put a finger over my mouth, motioning for me not to talk, although in that moment I was sure I'd forgotten how.

Once inside, I felt safe. I'd been completely terrified alone on the darkening streets but being with Bram made me feel better right away. He explained that my cousin had been taken away by the German police, and that he didn't feel safe, even though he wasn't Jewish. In those circumstances, he didn't feel safe at all.

"Bram, they took my mama and my aunt." I couldn't help myself. I had to tell someone. "They just came without warning. I took off my shoes and my cello is broken and they shot a mouse and my mama is... I don't know where she is, and I don't know what to do."

Bram stopped me and grabbed my shoulders. "It's okay, Sal. You're safe here."

I could finally breath, at least for the moment.

Bram was impressive – blond, tall, and broad-shouldered – an athletic, powerful man. He had always been kind to my family, and he made me feel welcome.

"Sit down. I'll get you something to eat. You must be hungry."

As he went into his kitchen, I realized I hadn't eaten anything for hours, and I was famished.

Bram soon returned with a plate of food. As I began to devour the bread and cheese, he sat down and leaned in closely. "Sal, listen carefully now. I am a member of the Dutch resistance."

I looked up at him in amazement.

"You must promise, right here and now, that you never heard me tell you a thing."

"Oh God, I promise Bram. Really, I do, I won't tell anybody, I swear it." I was stammering. "I'll do anything to stay here. Please."

"Okay, okay, don't worry, I trust you. I figure you've grown up a lot already from all you've been through."

I nodded. I had seen more in the past few years than kids living in a country without invaders. In fact, I'd seen more in the past few hours than I ever cared to see in my entire lifetime.

"Bram, tell me more."

"We're all Dutch citizens," he said. "Young, old, rich, poor, it doesn't matter. Jewish and Christian – we share a common dream of getting rid of these German occupiers."

"That's what Daniel said before he disappeared."

Bram wasn't paying attention to me in that moment. He jumped up and ran to the window, thinking he had heard something.

I froze again in fear, unsure what to do.

"It's okay. It's nothing."

"Is it true the resistance is attacking German soldiers?"

"We've been conducting raids on German soldiers, supply depots, and transportation centers, doing whatever we can to upset their operations."

"Were you ever on a raid? I swear I won't say a word."

"I was one of the people who tried to set the Amsterdam Town Hall on fire. One night, we took a small boat full of explosives up the canal. We rowed quietly so no one could hear us. The plan was to sneak inside the building after the police did their normal security check."

I sat enthralled by my cousin's story.

"We wanted to destroy all the files with the names and addresses of Amsterdam's Jews. We figured that if we could make these lists disappear, the Germans wouldn't be able to round anyone up for arrest and deportation."

"Exactly! What a fantastic idea."

"Yeah, you're right. We got ourselves into the building, got the fire started, and got out in time before anyone could catch us."

"What happened?"

"The fire was put out before it could spread, and all the records were saved."

"But you tried."

"Yeah, and we'll try again. That's why I'm in danger, Sal. There are basically two reasons I'm a wanted man here in Amsterdam. First, I'm married to a Jew, and second, I'm a suspected Nazi resister. It's becoming more and more dangerous for me to be seen in public, and if they find out I'm still living in this house, they will come and arrest me."

"Can't you stay with a neighbor?"

"Unfortunately I can't be sure about them. The Germans are paying Dutch citizens 30 guilders if they turn in a Jew in hiding or a suspected resistance fighter. They use the money from the Jewish bank accounts they've frozen."

"They took my father's money," I said. "All of it."

"It's not only Nazi sympathizers who do this. When ordinary people struggle to get food and basic supplies, they grow desperate, and sometimes that means turning in their neighbors to the Nazis. But that's enough for now. Go to sleep. You must be tired."

"I have to ask you something. Is Daniel part of the resistance?"

"I don't know. Really, I don't know one way or the other. Most of us operate in great secrecy. It's better if none of us knows too much. That way, if the Nazis catch someone, they won't be able to divulge too much valuable information."

"So, you don't know anything about Daniel?"

"Sorry, I don't. Listen, I'm sure one day you'll get to ask Daniel yourself."

"Yeah, hopefully..."

Over the next few days, I hoped that some other resistance fighters would show up and bring a report about Daniel blowing up a German tank on some canal bridge. But those were just the dreams of a lonely little brother.

That night was the first time I'd ever slept anywhere alone, without my family, or at least without Louis that one time we slept overnight in Eindhoven. Luckily, I was so tired I had no trouble falling asleep on Bram's couch.

I woke up abruptly when I heard what sounded like a convoy of trucks. Bram rushed in and told me not to move. He went to the window and peered through a tiny slit he had cut in the shade. Whatever danger might've been looming passed as soon as it came. Still, from then on, whenever Bram sensed peril – sirens in the streets, soldiers marching, or spontaneous shouting from his neighbors – he made me hide under the wooden floor of his kitchen. It was terribly cramped and stuffy in there but I understood that it might be the difference between life and death, between seeing my family again or not, so I didn't complain and remained hidden under the flooring for as long as Bram thought necessary.

Several days later, he came back home with disturbing news. "Sal, it's too risky for you to stay here, so I'm moving you to another house."

"Are you sure?" I was terribly disappointed.

"Sorry, but it has to be done. It's not far away and you'll be safe. I'll check on you as soon as I can."

That evening, just before curfew, Bram ushered me across the canal to a house on the Prinsengracht, just a few doors down from where Anne Frank and her family would eventually be discovered by the Nazi police.

For three weeks, I lived in a small apartment with Bram's cousin and her son. All day long, I stayed home alone with the young boy, while Bram's cousin went off with the resistance. Whenever a German patrol passed by the house, we had to hide away from the windows, careful not to make even one peep the soldiers might overhear.

Keeping a little boy amused while fighting boredom and the fear of arrest was nerve-racking. Dutch police headquarters was just across the canal. They could search us anytime, and I never knew when a neighbor might see me inside the house and report it.

The noose was tightening around the necks of Amsterdam's Jews.

20

Bram disappeared a few weeks later, turned in to the Dutch police by an unknown informant. He was kept in a local prison, but he arranged for me to move in with some of his Jewish friends. I never found out how he knew that where I'd been staying had become unsafe.

The Kessels, an upper middle-class family, were still able to live in Amsterdam because Mr. Kessel worked for the Jewish Council. His position entitled him and his family to certain privileges, and thanks to their odd good fortune, I was able to benefit.

Mr. Kessel and his wife registered themselves as my guardians, ensuring my safety, at least for the time being. They tried to assure me that I didn't have to worry about every police siren or pull the shutters tight each night when it got dark. They had no hiding place for me under the floorboards. Although I was still struggling to calm my fears, I tried my best to adapt to the habits of their household.

Mrs. Kessel was permitted to shop beyond the normal restricted hours for Jews, so she was able to buy plenty of food for us. I ate quite well and slept in a comfortable bed.

Soon enough, I began to feel like one of the family. Although I enjoyed the friendliness and creature comforts of the Kessel's fancy home, I was continuously haunted by not knowing the whereabouts or the condition of my own family. It was impossible to forget, and the questions nagged at me all the time.

Reports on a British radio station included news of more transports from the Dutch transit camp at Westerbork to the concentration camps in Auschwitz and Sobibor, both in Poland. Rumors were flying about who went where, and when, but nothing could be verified.

Even with his connections on the Jewish Council, Mr. Kessel couldn't help me get news of my family. The Germans controlled all the record keeping of the Jewish Council, even the information Mr. Kessel and the others were responsible for organizing.

No one knew what happened to Louis once he reported to the German authorities. No one knew where Daniel had gone, by choice through his work with the resistance or by deportation as a captured Jew. No one knew where Tinie had been taken after being removed from her hospital bed. No one knew the whereabouts of my father since he reported to the police. No one knew where my mother and aunt had been taken.

No one knew anything but we all knew too much.

21

May 5, 1943 began like most other days. The sun came up, the milkman made his deliveries, and daily newspapers were distributed throughout the city. But life for Jews in Amsterdam hadn't been normal for a long time.

We weren't allowed to walk on the sunny side of the street. There was no milk available to Jewish households, and headlines featured more and more bad news for the Jews of Europe.

I woke up early. After all, it was my birthday. Despite my bleak surroundings, I remained optimistic that I'd hear some word about my family. I still couldn't imagine they were gone and never coming back. Mr. Kessel had assured me that the news on the radio was probably exaggerated, and that Dutch Jews were being treated with respect. I wasn't so sure I believed him, however I appreciated his efforts to make me feel better.

I walked quietly into the kitchen to make breakfast. I didn't want to wake Mrs. Kessel and hoped she wouldn't mind that I was making myself comfortable. As I stood there, eating bread and cheese, I wondered about my family.

Were they hiding, staying in a work camp, or stuck somewhere in transit, not knowing what would happen next? Did Tinie's knee have a chance to heal? What about Louis? Was he in a place where he could play an occasional game of football with other boys? Was my aunt okay? Was Mama looking out for her? What about Bram? Perhaps he and Daniel were on a mission. Papa would be proud to know that his oldest son was fighting for our freedom.

As I finished eating, I felt myself smiling, imagining everyone together again after the war, swapping stories around our kitchen table.

Suddenly, I heard a sharp knock at the front door. I couldn't imagine who might be visiting at such an early hour. Everyone in the Kessel family was still sleeping.

All I could see out the window were two men I didn't recognize. My heart raced. Within seconds, my hands were sweaty. Bram would tell me to move away from the windows. I could hear my father warning me of the insidious nature of the German police.

The knocking repeated, strong, and forceful, against the Kessel's front door. I thought that if it kept on like that, I might see a set of knuckles blast through the door and grab me by the throat. I ran out of the kitchen and dove across the living room floor. My chest was heaving. I crawled on my stomach to get to a window and see who was there.

The rapping on the door repeated. On one knee, I could see a sliver of the outside. The two men were not Dutch. They dressed differently. They didn't look like anyone I recognized as a fellow citizen. They stood ramrod straight, as if they were members of a firing squad. They had to be German police dressed in plainclothes so as not to attract a crowd in the street. I knew from my father that the Nazis tried to avoid inciting panic or fear, as it disturbed their sense of orderliness and control.

The knocking came again.

"Salomon Kool!" I heard one of them call my name, as if I were just the next name on their expanding list of victims. "Salomon Kool!"

They had finally come to collect me – exactly on my 16th birthday. Ironically, through the diligent effort of Mr. Kessel and other members of the Jewish Council, the Germans knew the whereabouts of every Jewish citizen in Amsterdam. By officially making themselves my guardians, the Kessels had initially saved me from being taken away. They had also inadvertently made it easy for the Nazis to collect me the minute I came of age. And that moment had come.

"Salomon Kool!" The voice came again, accompanied by more knocking.

Males, 16 and older, were first in line for deportation. And the Nazis weren't wasting a second gathering up their next round of fresh-faced teenagers. I didn't look my age but that would not matter. I was now officially 16, which meant it was my turn.

Before they could yell my name again, I opened the front door. I had considered hiding but then my adopted family's house would've been violently ransacked. I thought it would be better if I gave myself up and spared everyone all that trouble. Besides, I figured they wouldn't keep me long. What use was I to them?

"Salomon Kool?"

I nodded. One man immediately grabbed me by the arm and pulled me outside into the street. Neither one of them said another word. While the Kessels were still sleeping, I was quickly removed from their house, on my way to who knows where.

Once again, I was alone. There would be no birthday party for me that year.

22

Since I was officially 16 years old, the undercover police officers treated me like any other adult, pushing me aggressively down the street before jamming me into the back of a small police van. As we rode through the familiar streets of Amsterdam, I imagined jumping out of the vehicle, rolling across the cobblestone streets, and disappearing into an alleyway.

But the reality of the situation quickly set in when we reached a collection point and two soldiers yanked me forcefully from the van. They passed me to another set of policemen, both even bigger than the two who plucked me from the Kessel's.

Everything was happening fast.

I couldn't take my eyes off the guns they were carrying. They looked terrifying. I was afraid to move in case I distracted one of them into firing his weapon. The shorter of the two barked something when he caught me staring at his pistol. I immediately put my head down and looked away.

Once inside the interrogation room, I thought my life was over.

"Stand here," one man said, pointing to the center of the room. "Don't move."

A different officer stepped forward from his desk and slapped me. "Where are your parents?"

I was too frightened to speak.

The officer slapped me again. "Where are they?"

I wasn't sure how to describe what had happened to them.

The officer was extremely impatient and slapped me again. He looked at me with such disdain. "Tell me where your parents are, Jew."

"I don't know. I don't know, really. Both of my parents were sent away but I don't have any idea where they are."

The officer knocked on the door of a small interrogation room. Two armed guards entered and grabbed me. They escorted me swiftly to the collection center. I remembered what my father had told me about this process. Everyone brought to the former Jewish theater would be sent on one of the weekly trains to Westerbork, a German deportation camp, built expressly for the Jews of the Netherlands. From there, most were sent to concentration camps in Poland.

But first, everyone had to be processed. Registration cards were checked, and duplicate lists were made with the names of the arriving prisoners. One copy was sent to the office of the Jewish Council, the other to Westerbork, along with the prisoners. Everything had to be signed by the Nazi commander, Ferdinand aus der Fünten.

The last time I had been in the theater was to see a show and celebrate my 14th birthday. Now, I saw how its interior had been gutted by the Germans to serve as a holding pen. My father was right. It had become a depressing place, full of people whose lives were destroyed.

It was terribly crowded. Among all the commotion, I noticed one man in particular, constantly besieged by his assistants with papers to sign and frantic mothers imploring him to help them stay with their children. I wondered who he was, and why he seemed so important. Was he working for the Germans or the Jews? Or both?

"Excuse me," I said to a woman next to me, waiting in line to be processed. "Do you know anything about that man?"

I pointed as discreetly as I could.

"His name is Walter Süskind. He works for the Jewish Council and he's in charge of organizing deportations. I don't know if he can help you."

"Thank you. Good luck to you."

"Good luck to all of us, dear boy."

Before I realized what was happening, Süskind approached and introduced himself. "What's your name, young man?"

He was friendly yet business-like as he asked about my circumstances.

"My name is Sal. I turned 16 today."

"Happy birthday."

Mr. Süskind was obviously disturbed to offer good wishes in such a place.

"Let's hope your next one is better."

Someone came up to him and he quickly signed some papers before continuing with me. He looked normal, dressed in an ordinary suit, of average height and weight, with light brown hair and normal features, yet he certainly didn't have a normal job. He seemed to be a man of great influence.

"You're officially eligible to be deported like any other adult but because you look so much younger, with your slight build and those big eyes – maybe you could pass for an under-age child."

"Okay."

I was thankful for anything that would save me from one of those trains.

"I guess I'm lucky to be so short. I'm barely five-foot-five."

"That's true, because registering you as an adult means immediate deportation. I'll arrange to have you removed from the list."

"Thank you, Mr. Süskind."

That was all I could say. In the middle of all the chaos, I wasn't sure what he was referring to but I knew I had to pay close attention to every word he was saying.

"Wait here. Be patient. One of my assistants, he's a graphic designer by trade, will forge new registration papers for you. When everything is ready, you'll leave the theater through a side door, walk around to the front of the building, and hurry across the street, directly to the crèche."

"The what?"

"The children's boarding house. A nurse from the crèche will accompany you. She's allowed to cross the street without being checked by the police."

"Thank you, Sir."

I was stunned by how fast everything was happening.

"I hope this arrangement will save you, at least temporarily," said Süskind. "But whatever happens, don't tell anyone your parents have been deported."

23

We left the theater through a side door.

"Don't look around when we cross the street," the nurse said.

She had soft features, with auburn hair and rosy cheeks but her voice was hard and without emotion.

"Tuck your arm inside mine and keep moving."

Perhaps in better times this woman was carefree and enjoyed life. Right then she seemed sobered by the conditions surrounding us. For just a second, I bristled at her speaking to me like a child and telling me what to do. I was shorter than her by several inches – shorter than most grown-ups at that point – and I may have been able to pass for her son but I was 16 years old, on my way to becoming a grown-up, so I didn't like anyone speaking to me like a child. Then again, my situation made the nurse a welcome figure, despite her tone. She was risking her life to take care of me, and she didn't have to. I needed all the help I could get.

We hustled down a narrow alleyway and came onto the main street, right next to the theater entrance. German soldiers were stationed everywhere. Some stood still and some milled about, pushing people left and right, barking orders to stay quiet and keep moving.

One large soldier looked as nasty and mean as I imagined a man could ever look. He made me terribly nervous but it wasn't only him. The entire atmosphere was intimidating. I tightened my grip on the nurse's arm.

"Keep your eyes down," she said sternly. "Please. Do not look directly at anyone."

I tried to avoid looking at everything, especially the penetrating gaze of that guard. We waited for the tram to pass and then we crossed the street. In a few seconds, we had made it past that threatening moment. I felt a tremendous urge to look back at the theater. If I could look at what had frightened me, maybe it wouldn't feel so terrifying.

The nurse sensed my impulse.

"Don't turn around. Let's go inside. Everything is all right."

As soon as we got through the door of the crèche, she turned to me.

"Sal, I'm sorry I've had to been so hard on you. In these situations, there's no room to be gentle. None. There's one way to go forward in such a risky situation and no second chance to get things right. I hope you understand."

She smiled warmly and then left me standing there, alone. As I looked around, I was overwhelmed by the sound of babies and children. The entire building seemed to be roaring with a mix of laughter, crying, shrieking, and singing. The babies were organized in one area and created a symphony of crying, cackling, whining, and more and more crying.

Try as they might, the nurses couldn't keep up. It was impossible to provide each baby with the attention they were used to getting at home. There were just too many to comfort. Some older girls, maybe eight or ten years old, helped the nurses by picking up the babies and walking them around, trying to calm them down.

It seemed like the babies could sense that they'd been forcibly separated from their parents, and that they may not be reunited with them again. I think they knew it, somehow. Their crying had an extra sound of desperation, which affected everyone in the crèche. The nurses had their hands full, comforting the babies and assuring the older ones that there wasn't anything to be afraid of, that the situation would improve, and that they would see their parents again soon.

I was now one of those children. I welcomed the reassurance, even though I didn't know if I believed what they were saying. One thing was sure: it was the only way to cope. All of us had been separated from our parents. Some of them were across the street, waiting to be deported. But many were already gone to Westerbork or another concentration camp.

According to one of the nurses, the Germans were accelerating the rate of deportations. During the past two weeks, more than 8,000 Jews had passed through The Jewish Theater collection point across the street. This meant that the crèche was overburdened, teeming with scared and confused children of every age, all suddenly left alone.

Walter Süskind managed to make my name disappear from the written records the Jewish Council provided to the Germans. I was one of the lucky ones. I would be safe, temporarily at least, inside the crèche. But if the Germans found out I was 16 years old and that my parents had been deported, I would be sent to Westerbork on the next train.

For the time being, I was satisfied still to be considered a child.

Although I was older than the other children, the nurses looked out for me. They understood how a boy my age could be affected by the situation just as much as a youngster, more so because I was old enough to comprehend many of the horrors that had taken place.

Word had spread quickly among the nurses and other workers in the crèche that I was 16, which posed a serious risk. Whenever one of them considered it necessary for me to hide, they made sure I was hustled away to a safe spot, most often up in the attic, far away from the places the German soldiers checked when they did their usual inspections.

I loved watching the nurses running around in their white smocks, looking so feminine and full of life. I enjoyed having access to them, unusual for a boy my age. Although I was somewhat shy, my subtle sense of humor endeared me to everyone.

I was placed with the younger children when it was time to sleep. As night set in, I wrapped my thin blanket tightly around me, surrounded in the large room by anxious boys and girls, crowded together on their small, uncomfortable cots, missing their parents.

24

"Where are your parents?!"

Every night, the German guards shook each child out of their dreams, one at a time, and frightened them all with their barking.

"Where are they? Come on, tell me."

It was always the same routine. I could never sleep until my turn had come and gone. I always heard the loud footsteps of the guards' heavy boots working their way up the stairs and into the large room where all of us were supposed to be sleeping. I often heard a nurse pleading with the guards to leave us alone – to no avail.

As the guards did their nightly bed checks, I pretended to be asleep. I was watching as they reached the top of the stairs and circulated up and down the rows of beds, clopping along in their noisy boots, asking the same question with heavy, robotic voices.

"Where are your parents?!"

The smell of alcohol and sweat was overwhelming as one of them came close to me. It was always the same hand I felt grabbing my shoulder – large and thick, with a tight grip. It was dark but I could see his black, bushy eyebrows and those eyes, chilling me with an icy stare. I heard him panting for air as he approached my bed.

Herr Schönhalter was the same guard who stood so menacingly in front of the theater on that first day when I was brought in for deportation. Now, as usual during the nightly checks, he stunk of cheap whiskey, which made me want to puke.

"Across the street! My parents are across the street at the theater."

Before Schönhalter could get the question out of his mouth, I blurted out what I thought I was supposed to say. Cursing, the drunken German leaned in to pester me more and left his foul odor lingering by my bed.

"My parents are across the street at the theater."

I kept my voice at a higher pitch than normal but not a high falsetto, which could have given me away. I was desperate to make sure he knew what I meant. Süskind's warning had stayed with me, and I didn't want to give Schönhalter any reason to think I was alone.

He muttered a few words I couldn't make out under his rancid breath. Thankfully, he straightened up and trudged on to the next child to wake them brutishly from their dreams, shocking them into another living nightmare.

I stayed in my bed, trying to convince myself that my convenient lie was true, that my parents were just across the street, together, and that everything would be all right, just as the nurses said. I repeated my fantasy over and over, convincing myself until I finally fell asleep.

25

Life at the crèche continued, unchanged. I played with the children, had long discussions with some of the nurses, and read whatever books I could get my hands on. And every night, I went through the same bedtime routine with the grotesque Herr Schönhalter.

Quite often, I saw Walter Süskind rush in and out, getting papers signed, delivering packages, and removing small bundles under his coat. I always wondered what all the activity meant – what such a man could be doing, so busy all day and night. He waved at me sometimes, and one day, he told me he would do whatever he could to help, however he offered no promises, and had no idea when something might happen.

I asked around every day for any word of my family. Although I tried to temper my hopes and keep realistic expectations, I never stopped believing they were alive and maybe not so far away. No one ever said it couldn't be true, so I kept believing.

A few weeks later, Süskind arranged a special meeting for me with the Jewish Council to see if they could do anything. I had no idea what they could offer but I knew that the crèche, was not a place for me to remain safely much longer. Help was welcome.

Right after breakfast, a small bread roll with a drop of sugar and a cup of tea, I was told to wait inside the kitchen. When the food truck came by with its weekly delivery, I was instructed to hide in the back seat and stay down until the driver said I could move. He would give me a lift to the council headquarters, south of Amsterdam.

Walter Süskind hoped that the council could save me from eventual deportation by issuing me an exemption stamp. They had the power to do so. Only Jews who had an official stamp could be saved from the weekly trains to Westerbork or the camps.

As soon as we arrived, the driver told me to leave the truck and hurry inside the back door of the building into a small room. It was the first time in weeks I'd been alone, and for a few minutes, at least, I enjoyed the peace and quiet.

Soon enough, the uncertainty of the situation got to me. For one very long hour I waited, nervous and perspiring, as if I were about to take a test to determine my future. I had an idea of what the Jewish Council might ask – where I came from, who my parents were, how long I'd been at the crèche, etc. – and I had no idea if my answers would do the trick and secure an exemption stamp. And if I did get one, what would I do with it? Where would I go?

Finally, the door opened, and I was brought into a larger room. I was surprised by the general mood. No one smiled. No one even looked up, much less spoke to me. They merely moved some papers about, and murmured to each other, with no expression, as if someone else controlled them. It was as if a higher power made them speak and made decisions for them, too.

They were Jewish refugees from Germany. They asked me the perfunctory questions I thought they would ask but barely more than that. I was still sweating, afraid that I had said too much or too little. After a brief deliberation, the woman in charge approached me.

"My boy, we can help you. We can send you to Vught, a work camp in the south."

"What did you say?"

I was totally shocked by what she said. My ears felt hot, as if I had been burned already by this disturbing news.

"That's it. We can send you to Vught."

"Consider yourself lucky, my boy," said a man with a thick German accent.

"What?" I was still shocked by their offer.

"We're offering you a way out of here. There's no future for you here in Amsterdam."

"No future." I repeated the words, not sure what they meant.

Vught had been established in January 1943 as a transit center and work camp for the Jews of Holland. During the month of May, while I remained in the crèche, worried about what might happen to all of us, the Germans gathered Dutch children and deported them to Vught. Everybody knew. I later found out that 1,266 Jewish children under the age of 16 had been sent from Vught to the Sobibor death camp, to be gassed as soon as they arrived.

When the people on the Council told me they could send me safely out of Amsterdam to Vught, I didn't know if that meant I had a future to determine.

As I bounced along on the floor of the food truck, returning to the crèche, I replayed the entire scene in my head so I could report it accurately to the nurses and perhaps to Mr. Süskind. Back at the crèche, Walter Süskind approached me after dinner.

We retreated to a corner of the room where the babies were being tucked in for the night.

He seemed terribly distressed. The Jewish Council's offer was not helpful at all. Vught was a known death camp. "I am deeply ashamed to hear such things, Sal."

"Mr. Süskind, it's not your fault. Thank you for giving me the chance to speak to them."

"No, there's nothing to thank me for, not at all. You see, I am a German too, I must confess. But of course, you knew that, didn't you?"

I said nothing.

"I am a German Jew but I am ashamed to speak the same language as these people. I am so sorry."

"Mr. Süskind, you've done your best, I'm sure."

He took my arm and pulled me into the kitchen. "There's one last way to avoid deportation. It's a secret and must be kept that way."

I nodded.

Süskind was more serious than I'd ever seen him.

"We have underground resistance workers shuttling children to hiding places all over Holland. You must keep a low profile, and not tell anyone, not even the nurses. Understand?"

"Yes."

"When it's the exact time to move, you'll know it."

"How?"

I stopped speaking. I trusted that Mr. Süskind was telling me everything he could. I would have to take a leap of faith.

"More than likely, the moment will come without warning in the middle of the night."

He turned and left the kitchen.

Once more, I was alone.

26

The noise in the crèche never stopped, and since there were so many children coming in and out each day, there was little relief from the commotion. The nurses did their best to keep the children occupied and calm but it was not an easy task.

Food was becoming scarce as the Germans restricted deliveries in the area. For a growing boy like me, this meant waiting my turn and allowing the little ones their portions before I had my own larger share. Some days, I had to wait until evening to get enough food to call it a meal. Once the children ate dinner and went to bed, the nurses dished out what was left for them and me.

During those hurried meals in the kitchen, wolfing down the extra food to be in bed before the guards made their rounds, the nurses told me stories about the secrets inside the crèche.

Sometimes, while milling around in the small courtyard, catching a whiff of fresh air and a bit of sunshine, I noticed the nurses handing packages over the back wall to someone on the other side. I always wondered what was inside those bundles, and who the nurses were giving them to but until then, I hadn't asked any questions because it really wasn't my business, and I was afraid of losing favor with the nurses.

I found one night that those packages were babies, wrapped in blankets and string, secretly ushered out of the crèche by the nurses and handed over the wall to members of the Dutch resistance. They delivered the babies to sympathetic families all over the country who were willing to hide them or raise them as members of their own family.

These babies were being saved from certain death. The crèche was not strictly monitored, especially during the day, so the nurses, Süskind, and other resistance fighters whose names I never knew, were able to maneuver their way through the existing system to save more than 500 children – wrapped up in blankets, suitcases, and even trashcans.

Although their job was dangerous, and any of them would've been killed instantly if the German guards caught them, the hardest part was convincing their parents across the street, awaiting deportation, to let their children be taken into hiding. It was an excruciating choice between two unknowns: stay together and go on a transport train, or give up their children to virtual strangers, without knowing whether they would ever see each other again.

27

As the summer wore on, daily life inside the crèche slowly changed. I didn't understand what was happening. The relentless activity I had initially observed steadily decreased. The nurses put their best foot forward but they were preoccupied by events surrounding them.

Without as many young, small children running around, it was becoming more and more probable that I would be noticed by the German guards, especially during the day. My presence was becoming more obvious, and riskier, too. The nurses felt it was safer for me to hide.

From my spot high up in the attic, where the guards could never see me when they inspected the lower floors, I could see everything happening in the street. I witnessed fewer and fewer people moving in and out of the theater and far less traffic in and out of the crèche. The steady stream of transports to the train station were becoming less frequent. I wondered if they had finally taken everyone they wanted.

My time was running out. I'd overheard the nurses saying it wouldn't be long before the Germans sent everyone to the camps. In the past week, even a few nurses had disappeared.

One hot July night, as I tried to sleep, I felt a cold hand slip over my mouth, and another grab my waist. I knew it wasn't the rough, heavy hands of Herr Schönhalter.

"You must leave tonight. Hurry. Good luck, Sal."

No explanation. As I sat up, I saw a silhouette heading for the stairs. Walter Süskind was in and out of the room in less than 30 seconds, telling me only what I needed to know.

I didn't have a second to waste. I packed my meager belongings and snuck down the stairs, shoes in my hands so I wouldn't make noise. I thought of the last day I had seen my mother, when the German soldiers approached, and she told me to remove my shoes before I climbed the stairs to my bedroom. This time wasn't so different.

I stopped as I approached the front door of the crèche. No one seemed to be awake, not even a nurse. I had no idea what to do. I knew I had to leave, yet Mr. Süskind hadn't said anything about where to go. I was completely on my own.

I kneeled down to stay out of view and looked outside through a crack in the window. One German guard stood watch on the other side of the street, in front of the theater. I waited to make sure no other soldiers joined him. I watched as the tram pulled up in front of the crèche, obscuring the guard's view for a moment. When the next one came by and stopped, it would be my best chance to escape. Slowly, ever so slowly, I opened the front door of the crèche, just wide enough to slip out, undetected, when the next tram arrived.

I began to sweat, worried that the guards would come to the crèche for their nightly bed check before I had a chance to escape. If I waited until after they came and went, the tram might not be running anymore, and I could be stuck inside another night.

Mr. Süskind sounded certain that I had to go right away. He must've known something about more deportations and wanted to make sure I was gone before I could be taken.

With the door cracked slightly open, I could hear the next tram approaching. My heart began racing, and I grabbed my small sack tightly in my hand. I would only have a few seconds to disappear before the tram pulled away and the guard had a clear view.

Timing my movements perfectly, I darted onto the sidewalk and quickly turned into an alley next to the crèche. I moved as fast as I could without running, my cap pulled low over my eyes, shoulders tucked, and my gaze focused forward. I had no idea where I was going. I was just going wherever I could, and as quickly as possible. I didn't know if I would bump into a German soldier at the next corner. What would I say if that happened?

I kept moving. I could be spotted by someone looking out a window. They could yell, "Jew! Jew!" loud enough for anyone to hear. I tried to move invisibly. No safe destination came to mind. As I walked further, Amsterdam felt like an abandoned ghost town.

I noticed that the bridges over the canals were raised up. One of the nurses had said that the Germans would try to trap all remaining Jews by lifting the bridges, making it impossible for anyone to escape. This would make the final round-ups easy for the Nazis. Jews running for their lives would have nowhere to go. With the bridges now up, I figured there wouldn't be a single corner of town left unchecked, and with the size of the army now rumored to be occupying Amsterdam, a citywide sweep could easily be completed by morning.

For now the streets were quiet, and I had no trouble steering clear of the handful of German soldiers who casually roamed the streets. And yet I could sense that this was just a brief calm before some terrible, final storm. Mr. Süskind's vague warning was becoming clear. The Nazis were going to round up all remaining Jews, once and for all. This was definitely the wrong night to be out on the streets of Amsterdam with no protection.

As I leaned against the window of an abandoned store, I caught a shaft of light to the Star of David on my jacket. I began to bite my way through the yellow thread fastened securely to my coat. Slowly, I managed to un-sew the badge and remove it.

I knew that every minute I stayed visible increased my chances of being picked up. But where could I go? Who could I wake in the middle of the night? If I rang the bell of a familiar house, how could I know I wouldn't be turned in by a new occupant? Even worse, by some scared friends?

I was lost. I may have been strong for a 16-year-old, made even stronger by my situation, but I was still a boy. Of all the adults who used to nag me every day, not a single one was around to look after me or offer even a morsel of advice.

As I considered the people who might offer me shelter, I only came up with one name I could trust and decided to take a big chance.

28

Every boy fantasizes about overcoming danger, just as our favorite adventure heroes do but none of us think we'll ever be faced with a real life-threatening situation.

I was scared that night, moving through a city that seemed unfamiliar and not at all friendly. Once I figured out what to do, it wasn't long before I was standing outside Hugo Koen's apartment, confident that this was my best chance to get help. I had no idea if my former gymnastics teacher was still in the city but I had to try.

I picked up a few pebbles from the cobblestone street and threw them softly at an open glass window. I whispered Mr. Koen's name as the tiny rocks landed with a clinking sound.

Suddenly, moving so fast it frightened me to no end, the window shut with a thud. Within seconds, the front door swung open and Hugo Koen appeared, staring coldly at me. He wasn't tall at all – I'd grown to his height by then – and for a moment, much to the surprise of both of us, we looked at each other eye to eye. For a second, I wondered if Mr. Koen even recognized me. It had been quite some time since we had spent our Sundays together.

Mr. Koen yanked me inside and shut the door. His grip was as strong as ever. He left the lights off and pulled me into the front room. I felt like I was being propelled through a darkened horror house at a carnival, like my older brother Daniel had done with my brother Louis and me, when we were young boys on a summer holiday.

"Sal, what are you doing here?"

"Mr. Koen, I'm sorry, I'm really sorry to disturb you like this but I was at the crèche, staying there, and this man, Walter…"

I stopped, thinking I shouldn't use any names, not even with someone I knew, to describe the secrets going on at the crèche.

"I came here because I have no other place to go. My parents are gone. Everybody in my family, I don't know where they are, and this man told me tonight I had to leave right away. It wasn't safe in that place any longer, and the Germans are everywhere, so I had to run and I didn't know where else to go. So, I'm here."

I stood in the dark, out of breath, panicked. I could barely see Mr. Koen's face and had no idea what he would say.

At first, he said nothing. He simply handed me a set of keys and guided me firmly to the front door. "You can spend the night in the gym at school. But listen. If you're caught, you must never mention my name, do you understand, my boy?"

I nodded and tried to say something but my voice wouldn't function.

"You must be out of the gym before school reopens in the morning."

My jaw dropped. Mr. Koen was Jewish, and he was putting me right back out on the street. The conditions he was offering wouldn't ensure my safety for more than a few sleepless hours. If I wasn't careful, and lucky, I might even get killed.

Hugo Koen wasn't the same man I remembered. He had always shown me special attention in the gym, as more of a mentor than a teacher but now I felt like a burden, an unnecessary impediment to his own safety, one he needed to eliminate.

Although I had excelled at gymnastics, I wasn't quite a professional prospect and Mr. Koen never saw that as a reason to turn me away from his training program. If he had chosen to train only boys who were potential Olympic athletes, his school would've remained quite small.

He always reminded us that not every kid in the world has a

chance to exercise, let alone compete. As a former journalist who had gone to Spain as a correspondent for a socialist newspaper in Spain during the Spanish Civil War, Hugo Koen had a bigger agenda than his tumbling and stretching curriculum. Only years later, as I came to see the world in a different light, did it dawn on me that somersaults and socialism were not one and the same.

None of that mattered anymore. Mr. Koen opened his front door, and without a word, he swiftly pushed me out onto the street. The door closed quickly, and I ran as fast as I could to the school. It was the first time in months I had stretched my legs and run, and it felt awkward. I was out of breath by the time I arrived. The keys rattled in my hands as I unlocked the door.

It was dark and cavernous inside. I refused to let the silence unnerve me. I wasted no time hiding in the first space I spotted – under Mr. Koen's desk in his office. I had to stay there until the sun came up or a Nazi soldier stood before me with a gun. I had no other choice.

I realized there'd be no more safety net for me, not from my parents, or from anyone else in my family. No one could be counted on – not my teachers, the nurses, or even Walter Süskind. I was on my own and facing a huge fear of the unknown.

I wanted to cry but the tears didn't come. I didn't don't know whether I was too scared or just too tired. I felt myself changing into some other being I didn't recognize, as if I were toughening up for a long trip to an unknown destination.

I once read a book about some adventurers who struggled for weeks to climb Mount Everest. Some of the men died along the way, from starvation or freezing weather. No matter how much they wished to climb the mountain successfully, none of them knew if they would survive and make it to the top.

I wondered if I was anything like those mountain climbers. I closed my eyes and fell asleep, waking up only once when I thought I heard a scream.

29

I heard many screams. Throughout the night, the Nazis rampaged through Amsterdam, rounding up Jews in a citywide sweep. People screamed for several reasons. Many had loved ones ripped away from them as soldiers took their family members to unknown destinations. Others could only watch as their houses were destroyed right in front of them. Some were beaten for any form of resistance. It was pure luck that the Nazis hadn't come near the school where I was hiding.

The windows of the gym were open, and the cool summer air was accompanied by the random sounds of gunfire, screeching tires, and German soldiers shouting commands. I drifted in and out of sleep, not always sure if I was dreaming. I tried to sleep again each time I was awakened but it wasn't easy. The memory of my mother and aunt being marched into the back of a truck was never far from my mind. Crouching under Mr. Koen's desk reminded me of how scared I had been that day, hiding behind the door of my bedroom.

I was petrified that they would find me in the school gym under the desk. If they did, I had nowhere to go. Yet, I knew I was safer inside than wandering the streets, asking for trouble.

The only thing that helped me sleep was pure exhaustion. Since arriving at the crèche, I was woken up every night by children with wet sheets, bad dreams, or both. After weeks of disturbed sleep, I was wiped out and slept through much of the horrible noise of that awful night.

When the light of a new day woke me up, I had no idea where I was. I sat up and bumped my head on the underside of Mr. Koen's desk. That reminded me. Rubbing the back of my head and shaking off the cobwebs from a fitful night's sleep, I craned my neck to get a look at the clock, hanging on the office wall.

It was 7:10 a.m. People would be entering the building any minute. Every school had its early birds, anxious to start their day as soon as possible. I couldn't risk being seen. There was no way to be sure whether a student or teacher might call the police and report a Jew in hiding. After all, the Germans paid a bounty to any Dutch citizen turning in a Jew. It wasn't much but hard times were hitting everyone, and moral codes were often compromised, especially for an extra ration of food.

I wasted no time in leaving the gymnasium and dropped the keys on Mr. Koen's desk as I walked out of his office. No one had entered yet, and when I slipped through the outside door, I discovered the streets were also silent. Only a few people were visible in the distance, walking to work or scurrying to catch a tram.

I turned the corner and walked but I had no idea where I was going. I pulled my hat down on my forehead, hoping to look like any grown-up on his way to somewhere important. The sun was not yet up, and I wrapped my lightweight jacket tight around me. I wasn't wearing my yellow Star of David. It was still stuffed in the pocket of my trousers.

I wasn't sure whether to put it back on. If I was wearing it, and was seen out on the street, I could be arrested immediately. If I was stopped on a routine check, and identified as a Jew, or at least accused of being one, I could be arrested for not wearing it – a double offense. But none of that mattered. I had no needle and thread, so sewing was impossible. Anyway, I had to keep moving undetected to find somewhere safe.

Some canal bridges had been lowered, so it was easy to go where I wanted, if only I knew where. I had to keep a low profile and avoid policemen or soldiers. Dutch police who became Nazis could be spotted by their distinctive black uniforms. For the most part, they left people alone. But the green-uniformed German police were intimidating. The Nazis also paraded units of soldiers throughout the city, dressed in brown uniforms and boots. They were a fearsome sight to behold, moving with impeccable precision. I didn't want to give them any reason to stop me.

At the corner of each street, I slowed down and looked in every direction before choosing which way to turn or to continue walking straight ahead. I tried to decide quickly and avoid looking suspicious. Whenever I heard sirens, or the telltale sounds of an approaching German army unit, I ducked into an alleyway and waited until the sound passed before moving again.

I felt as if I were traveling through a science fiction story from another country. On the one hand, I recognized all the familiar places I had been. At the same time, the streets were strewn with signs of last night's chaos, and it seemed like some invaders had taken over my hometown and turned it into a scary, foreign land.

The city was littered with people's personal possessions. I sidestepped several open suitcases with people's belongings scattered on the ground. I thought of my Aunt Rose, when the Germans took her from our apartment, struggling to carry her suitcase down the stairs, across the street, and into the back of a waiting truck.

I picked up a stuffed animal, dropped by a bridge, and wondered about the little child who would be missing it so badly. How could a harmless toy make any difference to the Germans? Yet it probably meant everything to a small boy or girl.

Near the canal, I spotted an apple and rushed to pick it up. I hadn't eaten much the past two days. I stopped before bending down to be sure I didn't appear too obvious. Luckily, no one was close by, so I grabbed it quickly, wiped it once across my shirt, and took a deep bite. I realized it might be all the food I'd have for a while, so I tried to eat it slowly.

My shoes crunched over bullet casings scattered in the street. I noticed pockmarks freshly made in some buildings. They came from bullets bouncing off the surface and taking bits of brick along with them.

People had been shot right where I was walking, only minutes or hours earlier. Real people, with real flesh and blood, feeling bullets go through them. Some had been shot trying to escape the Nazis. Would it be my turn next?

30

I stood in the kitchen of the crèche. With nowhere else to go, I had made my way back there, careful not to be seen, and arrived early in the evening. A weary Walter Süskind greeted me with a look of relief and agitation. "Sal, the situation is worse than ever. I'm sorry. There are no options left for you."

"Mr. Süskind, whatever you say. I'm just glad to be here right now. I had no choice about coming back."

"I know but after the raids last night, it's no longer safe for you to remain here. I think your only chance of survival is to become an *onderduiker*."

I hadn't heard that word in a long time. *Onderduiker* is a Dutch word meaning, "one who dives underwater" and during the war, it meant those who went into hiding. The only time I'd heard it used was when I was little, playing hide-and-go-seek with my brother and sister inside our house. Tinie always called Louis an *onderduiker* when he was hard to find. My mother called me the same thing when I was small and ducked my whole body under water in the bathtub. My past association with the word made no sense anymore.

"Sal, are you listening? Pay attention."

"I'm sorry, Mr. Süskind. I was thinking about my family."

"There is no time for that now. If you want to see your family again, first you must survive, yourself."

He was right. I had to survive.

"Wait here. I'll return shortly."

Despite the risk of transporting someone my age, Süskind decided to place me with members of the resistance who would transport me to a hiding place up north.

When he returned, Süskind handed me a pair of short pants that a 10-year-old schoolboy would wear. Because I appeared much younger than my real age, I could take the chance of traveling by train with two underground workers, posing together as a family.

"I hope they fit," he said. "You must sleep here tonight up in the attic, where the guards won't see you when they make their rounds. Tomorrow, you'll leave before they come back."

"How will I be sure to wake up?"

"A nurse will wake you."

Süskind smiled at my fear of oversleeping. "Good luck, Sal." He squeezed my arm and left the kitchen.

One of the nurses grabbed a piece of bread and a small slab of cheese and brought them along as she led me up three flights of stairs into the attic. The last set of steps was narrow and steep, leading to a small space under the roof of the crèche. The only light came through a small window at the top of the building, from a streetlight four floors below.

I crouched down to look out the window.

"Be careful, Sal. Stay down. Someone outside could see you."

I edged back, heeding her advice. I had learned to follow instructions. It started when my mother first saw the soldiers outside. It was the same with Bram, and Mr. Koen. All of them were extremely cautious about everything they did and made me act the same way.

"Wait here. I'll find you a blanket."

I smiled.

She handed me the bread and cheese. "Eat this before you sleep."

I was still hungry and gladly accepted her offer. Once she was gone, I fought the temptation to look outside and get more air. The attic was stuffy with the summer heat. After a few minutes, I couldn't help myself. I crawled to the window, and while lying flat on the floor I raised my head just high enough to see outside.

The Jewish Theater was directly across the street, guarded by a team of German soldiers at the front entrance. A few moments later, a tram passed by, stopped for a moment to let people off and pick up a few others, and continued to its next stop, five or six streets away.

I noticed in that brief moment, when the tram came to a complete stop, that I couldn't see the entrance to the theater or the guards standing watch. It was just like the night before, when I had left the crèche. I figured that, early the next morning, I'd have to do the same thing when I left with my new, underground "parents," taking me to safety up north. I worried about the tram schedule and whether it would make its usual stop.

What if no passengers disembarked and no one was waiting to board? Wouldn't the tram just keep on going right through its stop, giving us no chance to sneak by the guards?

The nurse, returning with a blanket and small pillow, distracted me from my anxiety. "Go to sleep now, Sal. You have to wake up early."

I listened to her footsteps descending the stairs. I thought of where I'd been the night before. I felt relieved to be back in the crèche with familiar people but being cooped up in the attic, all alone, wasn't comfortable.

I tossed and turned on the hard floor. My mind kept racing before I finally ran out of things to worry about. Under a summer crescent moon, the air slowly cooled. I pulled the blanket over my shoulders and thankfully fell asleep.

31

"Sal, wake up."

I rolled over in a panic, afraid I might've missed my opportunity to escape.

"You must go immediately. Leave the blanket and pillow and come with me."

I felt the nurse's hand on my shoulder and noticed her smell, a mix of my mother and sister. In that moment, I wanted more than anything to stay put, right there in the attic, safe and warm, and half-asleep.

"Sal," she said. "It's time to go."

I stood up, removed my shoes, and tiptoed down the stairs. The nurse took me into the kitchen to give me a small bag of food for the trip. Sitting at a table were two strangers, introduced as Ronald and Maria, who would be posing as my parents. Ronald was much taller than me, strong and stocky, with a trimmed beard and a crew cut. He looked like a serious soldier, uncomfortable with a day off from work. I hoped he wanted to help me.

"Good morning, Sal," he said. "We must go right away."

Maria looked closely at me. "We'll introduce ourselves properly once we're on the train. If anyone should stop us, do not speak.

Ronald has your papers, and he'll be the only one to speak, do you understand?"

I nodded, a bit frightened of Ronald but confident that this man knew what he was doing.

"Come, Sal," Maria said, taking my arm. "It's okay."

Her hands were as soft as her voice and she was as pretty as any of the nurses. I had no idea how old she was. She was certainly not old enough to be my mother.

We left the kitchen and exited through the back door of the crèche.

I'd been in the rear courtyard many times but had never considered the possibility of climbing any of the walls to see what was on the other side. One of them was definitely too high and someone had said it led to a long passageway to the back entrance of the Amsterdam zoo. The other wall bordered an alley leading to the front entrance of the theater. We couldn't go that way. We'd walk smack into a German guard.

"Follow me." Ronald took my arm and we moved toward the third wall, which had a small doorway. He took out a key and motioned for Maria and me to follow him. Suddenly, we were standing on the other side of the wall, facing another stone building. The door was open, and we walked right through without a sound. Maria and I followed Ronald down a set of empty hallways until we came to an exit door. He peered outside for a moment, and we followed.

I recognized the street. It was just around the corner, well out of sight from any German guards patrolling the exterior of the theater. We continued toward the railroad station.

"We just passed through a school next to the crèche," Maria said. "Members of the resistance discovered that the director is sympathetic to Amsterdam's Jews and he's trying to help in whatever secret way he can."

"He could get in terrible trouble," I said.

"Of course. But he's doing the right thing, you understand?"

"I think so."

I was beginning to realize the great risk so many people were taking by resisting the German plan to rid our country of all Jews.

"Last night," Maria said, "as you returned to the crèche and hid in the attic, the director of the school purposely left the back door of his building unlocked, as he has done almost every night, in case we need an escape route."

"You have to be so organized for any of this to work."

"That's right," Ronald said. "I considered it unsafe for us to leave through the front door of the crèche this morning."

"Why? I left there safely before. I waited for the tram to pass and..."

"We left before the trams begin their regular schedule. Without a way to hide, the guards would've seen us. We have an early morning train to catch, so this was the best route to take."

After the brutal *razzia* of two nights ago, when the Nazis raised the canal bridges and rounded up as many Jews as possible, the resistance considered Amsterdam to be in a state of total emergency. Any Jews remaining risked arrest and deportation, if not immediate death.

The long walk to the train station proved uneventful.

"Even the Nazis have to sleep," I said. "That must be why the streets are so quiet."

Maria motioned for me to stop talking as we entered the giant concourse of the railway station. Some soldiers were lolling about but none of them bothered to stop anyone.

Ronald, Maria, and I went straight to the departure platform and waited for our train. I felt safe with both of them.

32

My heart pounded as we disembarked the train in Roodeschool, a small town in the northeastern Groningen province. Dutch police and German soldiers were everywhere. Ronald, Maria, and I must've looked as if we fit right in because no one stopped us.

"How come no one checked us?"

"I don't know. Maybe we look like a nice Christian family."

"It doesn't matter. As long as it worked."

We walked in silence for 45 minutes, arriving at a farmhouse where we'd stay the night. It wasn't so bad, being out of the city and walking through nature. I enjoyed the burst of green countryside and appreciated the smells of the trees and animals.

As we sat in the large kitchen, eating soup and a chunk of bread, Ronald and Maria greeted some people they knew. I was amazed that everyone seemed to know everyone else, or if they didn't, after five minutes together, they seemed like old friends. Perhaps it was because they all had one thing in common – survival.

No one asked me anything. It was as if there was an unwritten code to mind your own business. I didn't really care, as I wasn't interested in sharing my story. I wished I could've asked each of them if they'd heard anything about my family. I suppose Ronald or Maria would've told me if they knew anyone who had news.

During the afternoon, more people arrived. The house was filled to the brim. At dinner, the kitchen was too crowded to hold even half of us. While some ate, others gathered around the house, discussing the ever-worsening war. I overheard one man describing how the Germans could pop up anywhere and anytime, rounding up whoever they pleased. I was glad they knew what was going on but I didn't like knowing that we were in danger, hiding in the farmhouse.

Ronald and Maria showed me a place to sleep in a small corner of the pantry behind the kitchen. Lucky for me, it was cooler than the attic in the crèche, and I fell asleep easily, listening to the crickets.

In the morning, we had to leave because the house was too full of other *onderduikers*. We all needed places to hide. Sadly there was a limited amount of space, food, and other supplies to keep us all healthy and safe.

Ronald, Maria, and I walked back to the Roodeschool train station. I noticed something was different. Yesterday, it seemed like we'd arrived in a sleepy little village. The atmosphere had changed overnight. We were stopped by a policeman as we entered the station. My hands were sweating as he checked our papers. Maria smiled as she took my hand in hers, trying to make it appear as if she was my mother or older sister. She looked at me, reminding me to relax.

While we waited for the train to depart back to Amsterdam, Ronald and Maria discovered that a German soldier had been mysteriously murdered in a nearby village, and that we could expect frequent security checks on our return trip.

"Sal, listen," Ronald said, pulling me close. "The ride back will be treacherous. The Germans will be searching everyone. Just keep quiet if you want to live."

"Let Ronald do the talking," Maria said. "Try to relax and keep your hands dry. You don't want to let them see you sweat, right?"

"No, I'm sorry about that."

"It'll be okay."

I liked Maria but I wasn't sure I believed her.

33

"So, boy, what do you have to say for yourself?" The soldier snapped at me, laughing, as he checked my forged ID card. "You like the Germans, do you?"

They hadn't wasted any time checking our papers. I was afraid someone would search the pockets of my trousers and discover the yellow Star of David crumpled up inside. I sat on my hands to keep the guards from seeing how sweaty they were.

"He's just a boy, Sir," said Ronald.

"What does he know?" Maria said.

For once, I was glad to be the dumb kid.

"Quiet!" the soldier barked, making all of us stop breathing for a second.

"I'm asking the questions here. The boy will answer me himself." The soldier stepped further inside our cabin and looked directly at me. "So boy, tell me. What do you think? You like the Germans?"

"Uh, I don't know, Sir." I tried to sound polite and natural.

"You see, Sir? He's just a boy. He doesn't know how he feels about something he knows so little about."

"I'm speaking to the boy, not you. Your answer, boy. Let's have it."

"Yes Sir, certainly."

I tried not to breathe too loud, fearing it would show how nervous

I was. If I wasn't Jewish, why should I be nervous or have anything to fear?

"I think so, Sir. Yes, I think so." I nodded, trying to convince myself that my answer could satisfy the soldier. "I like the Germans. Of course, I do."

"Good!" The soldier stared down at me. "Smart boy." He turned abruptly and snapped his heels together. "Heil Hitler!" He said it to no one in particular but I felt sure it was a warning to me that next time I would not be so lucky.

I was sweating profusely. Ronald and Maria appeared relieved, knowing we'd dodged such a close call. We'd seen other passengers removed from their cabins for unknown reasons, perhaps because they simply hadn't answered a soldier's questions satisfactorily.

"Good job, Sal." Ronald smiled at me for the first time.

"Your answer was eerily believable," Maria said. "I'm glad he didn't see your hands."

"I hope there'll be no more interrogations until I'm standing in the kitchen of the crèche, explaining all of this to Walter Süskind. I think I've answered enough questions for a lifetime."

34

"Hey Sal, you love it here too much to leave us?"

Sabine was one of my favorite nurses in the crèche and an excellent cook. I was happy to see her after secretly returning with Ronald and Maria. They had to figure out another option for where I could go.

"Can you fix me something to eat?" All I could think of was my aching stomach.

"Why are you back? Oh, never mind. I'm sure there's a good reason and I'm glad to see you but I wish you could stay in one place until this ugly war is finished."

"You and me both, Sabine. They couldn't find a hiding place for me. There's hundreds and thousands of Jews scrambling to find safety, and there's limited space for us."

"Eat, sweet Sal." Sabine handed me a small slab of cheese and the end of a loaf of bread. "It's not much but it's all we've got tonight."

I thankfully ate what was available and walked into the main room, which felt too quiet. "Where is everyone? There are hardly any children left."

"The situation has changed dramatically," said Greta.

She had been there since I had arrived and was always so patient

117

and positive. However, that night, she seemed especially tense and sad.

"Slowly but surely, the number of children is decreasing. Each day, it seems as if another one is taken across the street to be deported."

"It's like a terrible leak in the dam, isn't it?"

"It is, and we can't stop it. Mr. Süskind is working to secure places for as many children as he can. Sadly, as you know, there are never enough."

With no safe alternative, I remained at the crèche.

Throughout the summer, the nurses worried more and more about the resistance finding places for all the children, including me.

35

The German soldiers were about to collect all remaining children in the crèche. My heart raced as I scrambled up to the attic rafters to hide, hoping they would still ignore this spot. I was barely in place when they banged through the front door, barking out orders while they spread out across the lower floor. They ordered the nurses to take the crying babies out of their cribs. Some did as they were told. Others screamed, pleading with them to spare the children. The soldiers ignored them and pushed everyone violently out the front door.

The nurses brought out more babies until there were none left. Then, the soldiers commanded the nurses to go upstairs and gather up the toddlers and older children. When a nurse didn't move quickly enough, a soldier pushed her harshly to go faster. If a child held on too tightly to one of the nurses, they were yanked away and had to go down the stairs alone. The soldiers ordered the nurses outside. Two of them led a final group of toddlers into waiting trucks.

Suddenly, the entire crèche was silent. What had been a noisy flurry of chaos and suffering a moment ago was now deathly quiet. Not a single person remained.

Only me.

A lone soldier stepped back inside, checking to be sure the crèche was entirely vacant. I was afraid to breathe. The soldier turned abruptly toward the entrance, apparently satisfied that the building was empty. He snapped his heels together, and slammed the door shut as he left.

It was September 29, 1943, almost five months since I was first brought to the theater across the street and rescued from deportation by Walter Süskind. I had grown fond of the nurses and even came to enjoy the children. Each time I had been forced to return after attempting to escape, I felt like I was coming home. Now, once again, I was alone.

The latest move by the German army had taken everyone by surprise. First, they had made a final round-up of all the Jewish adults still inside the theater. They were herded onto trucks that took them to trains bound for Westerbork and concentration camps in the east. Everyone had to leave, without exceptions. Even members of the Jewish Council, who hoped they were exempt from deportation, were forced to go. No one could escape the net of the Nazis.

I peeked outside the window and watched an endless line of people being loaded into a caravan of trucks. It was nearly dark by the time the last one drove away, taking its passengers to what might well be their final destinations.

I curled up in a ball and didn't move until the next morning.

36

A police siren startled me out of a deep sleep. By the time I crawled to the window to see what was going on, there was nothing to look at. It must've been just a passing police car with no connection to the Germans. There were no guards standing watch. Not a single one. The army vehicles were gone, too. I was puzzled. I never imagined that once all the Jews were evacuated that the Germans would also disappear.

I couldn't stay in the attic forever. As soon as I felt how hungry I was, I ran down to the kitchen, expecting to find some food: everything was gone – no plates, no pots and pans, and definitely no food. It was as if the entire crèche no longer existed.

I saw a few people outside going about their business, but everything German was gone. The guard post, the wooden street barriers that blocked the road when they loaded trucks for deportations, the vans, trucks, even the guards. Not a trace remained, except a sign proclaiming the tram forbidden for Jews. That reminded me that the Germans still occupied Amsterdam, even if there was no trace of them nearby.

My entire stay at the crèche had been erased. A whole piece of my life was gone, with nothing I could hold onto, nothing to show where I had been and who had been there with me.

"What do I do now?"

Hearing my own voice echoing in the empty building scared me, as if a Nazi soldier was hiding somewhere, waiting to pounce. I knew that was impossible, that all of them were gone, yet the feeling was chilling.

No one remained to give me advice. Even Walter Süskind and his family had been forced to leave. I thought maybe they had been erased, too. Had everyone been erased?

I figured that just because the German army had left the area the city was probably just as dangerous as ever, if not more, for its Jewish citizens. After thinking they had rounded up every Jew, the Germans would be angry to find anyone who had avoided them. Once I stepped foot outside the crèche, I would have to know exactly where I was going.

"This is my city," I said to no one. "I can go wherever I choose." I began pacing back and forth, desperate to figure out where that might be. "Wherever I choose!"

I repeated this loudly, trying to convince myself that it was possible. I slumped against the front door, with no clue where to go. I couldn't risk returning to our old apartment, which must have been totally ransacked anyway. Bram was gone. Mr. Koen wouldn't want to see me again. I didn't know where any of the nurses lived, but that didn't matter because as far as I knew, they'd all been taken away with the children.

I sat for what seemed like hours, agonizing over who I might know still living in Amsterdam. I was growing more and more hungry. I searched the kitchen one last time, however the Germans had been thorough and not a single scrap of food remained.

Suddenly, I remembered the Kleins, friends of our family before the war. Like my father, Mr. Klein had been a passionate member of the Socialist Party, and I thought he might have found some clever way of surviving the deportations.

As I stepped outside the crèche, I realized I would never return. But I had no time to dwell on that. I had to focus on where I was going. It was like stepping into the ocean at night, without a moon overhead, when it's totally dark and you can't see the water until your feet are already in it. I had done that once when I was a little boy on a family trip to the North Sea. Papa took me by the hand and walked me from the sand dunes into the ocean. I was terrified and excited to be venturing into the unknown. Only this time, no one held my hand, and I was stepping into a situation I knew nothing about.

Thankfully, luck was on my side once again.

The Kleins lived close to the crèche, and I found their house easily. Mr. Klein worked with the resistance, and so far, he and a few colleagues had escaped the Germans through some complicated maneuvering around the city. They took me under their wing and promised to arrange a hiding place for me. Best of all, they had food. Despite shortages all across the city, they had managed to stockpile a supply of bread and cheese, and I made the most of it.

The next morning, they woke me up early. We had no time to waste, getting me out of the city. I had learned not to question anyone in the resistance because they seemed to know what they were doing, and besides, what choice did I have?

A university student accompanied me on a train to a small village in the southern province of Limburg. She was secretive, like many in the resistance, referring to herself only as, "Auntie Miep." She seemed much too young to be anybody's aunt but that didn't matter.

I was thankful for her help. I understood why most members of the resistance protected their identities. They were also saving people like me from knowing too much. Still, I wished I could've found out more about them. I wanted to know them all like my real family, who I missed so dearly.

37

As the train made its way south through the Netherlands to Limburg, I drifted in and out of sleep. Each time we stopped at a station and new passengers came onboard, I woke up, frightened that someone might wonder who I was, and call one of the guards to investigate.

I was not wearing the yellow Star of David, but I still felt conspicuous, as if the spot on my jacket where it had been sewn would be obvious to anyone, incriminating evidence that I was a Jew. But a simple matter of timing provided good luck, yet again.

Over the past year, the Germans had systematically rid the small towns and villages of their Jewish inhabitants, herding them up and forcing them to move into Amsterdam or another large city. Despite that, local police and German patrols were on the lookout, determined to capture each and every Jew who was still alive.

However, on that day, "Auntie Miep" and I arrived at the train station as the soldiers were changing shifts. No one paid any attention to the departing passengers, so we left without being checked. We walked for nearly an hour before arriving at a farmhouse in the middle of nowhere. I was anxious to find out who was there and if I could stay longer than 24 hours.

The house was full of resistance fighters. Two of them brought me into the kitchen, where they sat me down to explain the situation. "Your name is Sal, is it?"

The shorter man had a friendly smile and I nodded and smiled back at him.

"I'm Lars. Salomon Kool, eh?"

I jumped out of my chair, thinking he might know Daniel.

"Well, that's not your name anymore. From now on you'll have new identity papers and a new name."

"That's right, young man," said Hans. "From now on, you'll be known as Toni De Boer. We'll have everything ready soon, and by tomorrow morning, you'll be moved to a nearby town where we hope you can stay."

I nodded, I was glad to hear I might have a safe place to stay and disappointed that neither one of them knew Daniel or would say so if they did.

"No guarantees of that, you know," said Hans. He handed me a cup of tea and a chunk of bread. "We'll do the best we can to keep you in one place but you know how it's completely uncertain out there from one day to the next. We don't like it any better than you."

"Okay Sal, I mean, Toni," Hans said. "You need to learn who Toni is, in case you get stopped. It can happen any time and you mustn't give the police any reason to be suspicious."

Lars shook his head. "All it takes is one little reason to open their eyes and start wondering who you are, where you've come from, and especially what you might be hiding."

Hans nodded.

"You can't get any of this wrong. It's a question of survival."

"Okay." I was shell shell-shocked by the intensity of these two men.

"Okay? That's all you have to say?"

"Hey kid, you need to understand the big picture."

"Okay, I understand what you're saying, but I need to think a second."

I knew that Walter Süskind never exaggerated the horror of the war, and even though I understood how dangerous it was, I couldn't fully grasp how these awful conditions applied to me, a normal kid from Amsterdam. How could I be so hated and pursued by the Germans?

"You okay?" Lars said. "Try not to think so much. It'll make you more afraid."

"The situation is horrible," Hans said. "That's no secret. Just concentrate on living one day at a time and doing whatever is necessary to make that happen."

"I understand. Both of you are right. What do I have to do now?"

"First, your name. It's Toni De Boer. You were born in Venlo, a town near Tegelen."

"How many brothers and sisters do you have?"

"You mean for real? You mean me or Toni?"

"You, for real, how many?"

"Two brothers and one sister."

I was sure I would never forget them, no matter how my name was changed.

"Okay, let's use that. It will be easy for you to remember. So Toni, you have two brothers and one sister. Use their names and ages too, okay?"

I nodded, happy to be able to carry that information with me to help me survive.

"Toni, you are from Venlo, and you're working for a family in Tegelen to earn more money for your family during this difficult war."

"What kind of work?"

"Farming, I guess. Working on their farm, helping them because their other children were killed in the war."

"You'll know all of this in case you ever get questioned?"

"I will."

I reached out to shake their hands. "Thank you."

"Stay here and eat something," Lars said. He stood up and headed toward the kitchen door. "We'll be back to let you know when the papers are ready."

As I sat at the kitchen table, I thought about how the resistance was making me into a different person, at least on the outside. Although I understood it was necessary, I wasn't entirely comfortable with it. I didn't know how to become another person. I was glad I wasn't famous. They would've had to cut my hair and break my nose or something to make me look different enough to avoid being recognized. I thought that would be terrible.

I sat and drank my tea, trying to become Toni De Boer.

38

Early the next morning, Lars drove me to the nearby town of Tegelen.

"Everyone I spoke to thinks you'll do fine with this new family. You should be able to stay there for quite some time."

"How about as long as it takes for the war to end?"

"Yeah, that would be nice."

"Then I can be Sal Kool again."

"Okay, but for now you're Toni."

"Yeah, of course I am. Toni."

"Go ahead. Say it again."

"Huh?"

"Say your name. Introduce yourself."

"Hi, my name is Toni."

"Again."

"My name is Toni. I'm Toni. My name is Toni."

"Good. Just a few more times."

"Hi, my name is Toni. Toni de Boer. My name is Toni de Boer. They call me Toni. Is that enough?"

"That'll work. We're here. It's time to meet your host family."

"Thanks, Lars. For everything."

"Glad to help. Be careful."

We went inside, and Mr. Pfeffer and his family welcomed me with a lunch of soup and bread. They embraced me as a new member of their family.

"Hello everyone. My name is Toni."

I told the Pfeffers the story of my life, as Lars and Hans had instructed. They politely listened to me run through my new autobiography as Toni De Boer and then assured me that they understood my situation, and that I wouldn't have to worry about playing a role for them.

Mr. Pfeffer smiled. "We'll call you Toni, of course, to avoid the chance of any accidental slipups in front of unknown strangers."

"Thanks, Mr. Pfeffer."

"But for now, it's best for you to make yourself useful right away."

"I'd like to do that."

"Good, because if anyone should happen to pass by, it will look much better if you seem to fit into our daily life. Ready to work?"

"Ready."

Mrs. Pfeffer and her oldest daughter, Katrina, took care of the kitchen. The two youngest children tagged along for whatever snacks they could get in exchange for doing simple chores.

"Toni, go with Paul and Marco. They'll tell you what to do. I'm taking two of my middle children outside to attend to the animals and the vegetable fields."

"Thanks, Mr. Pfeffer, whatever you say."

The two oldest sons, Paul and Marco, worked full-time as blacksmiths in a shop adjacent to the house. Although Lars had told me I would be doing farming work, this seemed like an opportunity to try something else. I stepped inside their shop and was greeted by a blast of heat, fire, and smoke but I didn't mind. The air was getting cold outside, and with winter coming, this would be a warm place to work.

Paul and Marco made agricultural tools for farmers, iron rims for vehicles, and household items, such as fireplace racks, pothooks, utensils, and decorative wrought iron. They also repaired iron objects for their neighbors.

Soon enough, I was able to learn the tricks of a new trade – casting, bending, and welding, as well as pumping the bellows to fan the fire in the large brick hearth. I was strong from years of doing gymnastics with Mr. Koen, able to lift the heavy tools, some of which weighed as much as 12 pounds.

The Pfeffer brothers were happy to have me as an apprentice, and the work took my mind off my troubles.

39

The Pfeffers ran a small pub nearby, open three evenings a week. They offered a hearty, country-style supper menu, followed by live music and dancing. The sight of people filling their plates and singing and dancing made it seem like the war wasn't happening, even though Tegelen was just a few kilometers from the German border. It was as if this little town, tucked away in the southern-most province of the Netherlands, was living a fantasy life, undisturbed by the atrocities taking place nearby, if not right underneath its nose. With people coming and going, and the Pfeffers treating me like one of their own, I felt safe. There was no immediate danger to worry about, and no one thought much of a new face in the crowd.

I eagerly pitched in on performance nights, helping the traveling musicians load and unload their instruments and personal luggage. One night, I was pleasantly surprised to discover the owner of the trunk I was struggling to carry into the pub. "Miss Miranda" was a famous traveling singer who had caught the ears and eyes of many men. At the age of 16, I was no exception, and hoped to have my chance to meet her. Just as I was about to put her trunk on the floor, she passed by close enough for me to get a more than ample whiff of her perfume.

"Hi there," she said sweetly.

I looked around for a second to make sure no one else was standing there. The way she greeted me made my arms shake under the weight of her trunk. She was against the wall, posing and smiling. I knew she was looking at me because I was the only one there. Suddenly, her huge trunk felt light as a feather.

"Now don't forget, sweetheart, be gentle with my things, will you?"

My jaw must've dropped to the floor. I was so mesmerized by "Miss Miranda" and her magical presence I completely forgot that I was holding her luggage on my shoulder. It started slipping, and as I crouched down to catch it, the trunk fell directly on my left hand, flattening the tip of my pinky finger.

The whole world stopped. One second ago, I'd been staring dreamily at "Miss Miranda," hanging on her every word. A second later, I was in shock, staring down at the bloody mess that was now the remains of my fingernail. Without warning, I fainted.

40

I opened one eye and shut it. Something looked different. I opened my eye again, moved it right to left, and recognized that I wasn't in the pub any longer. It wasn't night, either, because it was much too bright where I was. And I was lying down – in a bed. I had no idea where I was, how I got there or who the bed belonged to.

As soon as I used my left hand to boost myself up, I found out. "Oh my God! My finger!"

It hurt like crazy. That's when I remembered what happened the previous night in the pub with "Miss Miranda," urging me to be gentle with her trunk. I realized I was in a hospital bed, inside an actual hospital. I was a bit dizzy from the lingering effects of the anesthesia I'd received, so I dropped back down on the pillow. I had to smile at my foolishness.

"You look pretty pleased with yourself, young man." A nurse came bounding into my room. "Feeling better, are you?"

"Better, I guess, yes." I was totally embarrassed, as if the nurse had seen what I did the previous night. "I'm a bit dizzy but thanks."

"You've come a long way back from never-never land. You know, you gave us quite a fright last night."

"What do you mean? I hurt my finger in the pub. That's all I remember. Did something else happen?"

The nurse smiled and moved closer. "We had a close call with you during the night, a very close call."

"What? Did I almost die or something? Come on, my finger got crushed, not my brain."

"Well, it just as easily could've been. You have no idea how you were acting last night."

"Tell me!"

"You were out of surgery for about an hour, and you were delirious."

The nurse was middle-aged, with short, brown hair and soft, kind eyes. "You were still under the effects of strong anesthesia and apparently you began hearing voices and seeing things."

"No, you're kidding." I laughed. I was afraid I might have revealed more than I should have. What if they found out I was really Salomon Kool, a Jew?

"Oh, I'm not kidding at all."

"Hearing voices and seeing things? I'm sure I didn't do anything like that."

I hoped the nurse would agree and admit she was just teasing me.

"You were acting strange from the drugs. Completely strange. You thought you saw nuns in the hallway, and you were talking to them."

"What was I saying?"

"Oh, I don't know. You were in and out of consciousness so we couldn't understand you. One minute you claimed that German soldiers were taunting you, and then you raved about a girl you had a crush on back in Amsterdam."

"You must be joking."

"No, not at all."

"But I don't have a girlfriend back in Amsterdam."

"It became quite serious, Toni. In the middle of all this chaos, the Germans made a surprise visit to the hospital."

"What did you do?"

"We all froze, naturally. We didn't know what to do. We couldn't shut you up without putting a pillow over your mouth."

"Thanks for not doing that." I smiled.

"Well, it wasn't funny at all. The German police moved down the hallway toward this room. You wouldn't stop ranting and raving. You suddenly sat up in your bed, going on about your mother crouching under the window as the Nazis gathered in the street."

"What?"

"Yes, you screamed and cursed. You were moaning about the terrible Germans."

"Oh, my God, I'm sorry. I could've gotten us all killed."

"Luckily, the police didn't hear you talking about your mother, so they couldn't put two and two together. Otherwise, you wouldn't be here right now."

"Maybe none of us would."

"You're probably right."

"One of them asked me what was wrong with you. I told him that you'd hurt your finger in a horrible accident and that the medicine was making you crazy and that your father had been killed during in the war and you just missed him, that's all. Just the anger of a wounded young boy who didn't understand war."

"I'm so sorry about screaming."

"You were lucky, Toni, or whatever your name is, that he didn't ask more questions. Now rest up, and we'll get you out of here later today."

I was aware of how close I had come to being taken away. The nurse knew I was Jewish, and could have turned me in, but she didn't. She chose not to. I was relieved to know that there were still Dutch people willing to protect Jews, as she and her co-workers had done for me.

I thought about how she described me to the German police: a boy who missed his father terribly, who was angry about a war he couldn't understand.

41

The next day, with my finger sufficiently healed, I returned to the Pfeffers' house in time for dinner. Just as when I first arrived, the entire family greeted me kindly. Even though the nurses had taken good care of me and protected my identity, I was so relieved to be out of the hospital and hopefully far away from any German police.

However, I soon discovered from Mr. Pfeffer that the situation for *onderduikers* in the south was as bad as it was in Amsterdam. The Germans knew that Jews were being hidden all over the country. It wasn't only dangerous for me. If the Pfeffers were found to be hiding someone, they would also face terrible punishment.

For everyone's safety, I faced a new set of rules. It was no longer safe for me to be seen in the pub. The Germans had infiltrated everywhere, and because local citizens were known to expose Jews it was impossible to know who could be trusted.

Until my finger fully healed, I wasn't able to work in the blacksmith shop. Cooped up inside the house all day, I grew unbearably restless. Although I didn't mind helping Mrs. Pfeffer with the household chores, I wanted to do something more.

The Pfeffer boys teased me about "Miss Miranda" and how she had missed me and couldn't find anyone to carry her trunk like I had.

Even though I enjoyed the attention, I didn't find it so funny. With the war intensifying, I felt more than ever like a marked man.

The air raid sirens never stopped; Allied planes flew constantly overhead on their bombing runs into Germany. Local resistance was growing as they organized their actions against the Nazis. I wanted to participate, but it was considered too dangerous for me to leave the house.

I insisted, however, urging Mr. Pfeffer and his colleagues to include me. I pointed out how I had escaped from the Nazis when they took my mother and aunt, how I had found my way, alone, on numerous occasions in a big city like Amsterdam, and most importantly, that I needed something to do, that I was going stir crazy inside the house all day!

Mr. Pfeffer was reluctant but he finally gave in. I was assigned the job of transporting homemade cigarettes to resistance fighters stationed by the river. For them, having something to smoke was just as important as having something to eat, so my mission was not frivolous, and I was encouraged to take it seriously.

I needed no reminder. What a challenge and honor to be part of the resistance! Finally, I had a chance to contribute to fighting the Germans. And each time I rode off on my bicycle, I could forget, at least temporarily, about being an orphan.

42

"Stop!" A man shouted as I rode past him.

"Halt!" Another voice was louder than the first.

I knew something was wrong and pedaled faster. I had no idea who they were or how I could possibly escape.

They were riding motor scooters so there was no chance to get away. The two men looked imposing in their leather jackets on top of their bikes.

I kept moving and noticed that they were Dutch policemen. I didn't know what else to do, so I just kept pedaling my bike.

"Stop! We're the police, you stupid fool!"

They gunned their motors and rode up close to me, one on each side, trapping me in the middle.

I kept riding, and so did they.

"Show us your papers. Now! Get off your bike."

My head was spinning, wondering what to do, if there was any way to escape.

"Come on, boy, you need to cooperate."

I wasn't about to do any such thing. I remembered riding like crazy with Louis, racing through an open field, right next to each other. Both of us jockeyed for position, daring each other to make a move and get an edge in our race to the end of the field. Suddenly,

Louis lurched to his left, and just as I reacted, he pulled to his right. He had totally faked me out and forced me to brake, impeding my progress. Louis took the lead and never gave it up, at least for that day.

"Halt, and show us your papers!"

I said nothing. I looked straight ahead and continued pedaling.

"Stop! Where are you going? Why are you afraid?"

Louis was with me, leading the way, so I took an enormous risk. I sped up, challenging both policemen to make another move.

"We will shoot you if you don't stop!"

I didn't care. I picked up my pace, gripping the handlebars in fear. They had no trouble keeping up, and I thought one of them reached for a gun. I wasn't sure but I couldn't slow down to find out. I veered sharply to my left and nearly hit the policeman. He skidded to avoid a collision. I slammed on my brakes, and the policeman on my right zoomed past. I put one foot on the ground, turned my bicycle completely to the right and took off as fast as I could.

The police wiped out on their scooters when they struggled to avoid hitting each other.

I pedaled like a madman, like I had a few years ago when Louis and I rode all the way to Eindhoven. I lost the policemen in a maze of fields and farms scattered through the countryside.

Finally, after riding furiously for nearly an hour, I arrived back at the Pfeffer's house, completely panicked and out of breath. The sack of cigarettes remained undelivered, and I had to explain what had happened.

"Come on, Toni, we need to know."

Mr. Pfeffer looked concerned. He called in two resistance fighters and the four of us sat in the kitchen. This wasn't some boyish prank we were about to discuss. Without anyone having to say so, I knew I'd put everyone in danger.

"I don't know how it happened. It was so fast. I was riding along, heading toward the river, like usual. Then these voices came out of nowhere."

"Germans?"

"No, they were Dutch police but the ones working with the Nazis. I knew it by their uniforms and the way they spoke."

I described how I avoided them.

Even though Louis would've been proud of me, it didn't change the mess I had made.

"Okay, Toni," Mr. Pfeffer said, "this isn't good. We're relieved you escaped but I think it's clear that you'll have to leave. You can't stay here, anymore."

"What?" I was shocked by the suddenness of his decision.

"Toni, we've seen something like this before. Maybe the police were playing with you, maybe they weren't. We don't know. We can't take any chances either way. We can't be sure if they know where you've gone. They may know right now that you're here."

"Are you sure?" I was desperate to hear Mr. Pfeffer change his mind.

He pulled his chair close to me and put his hand on my shoulder. "I'm sorry, Toni. As soon as we can secure a place, you'll be on your way. It's not safe here anymore. I can't risk my family. I'm sorry about this."

I was horrified at the thought of leaving.

They nodded.

A few hours later, everyone gathered for dinner. Looking around the table, I felt like begging for the first time in my life. The idea of leaving my new family made me sick. The war had taken away everything and everyone I had ever loved, and I had no idea if I would ever find a situation like this again.

After dinner, while waiting to leave, I sat alone in the blacksmith shop. I swore to myself that I would not grow close to anyone again. I couldn't. Leaving hurt too much. I couldn't lose anyone anymore. I'd lost enough already.

43

By the next morning, "Toni de Boer" had become "Johannes van Diepen." Resistance fighters forged new identity papers for me and secretly brought me to a new house. Along the way, they filled me in on my next host.

Paul Rose was a popular figure in the village of Tegelen, struggling to keep his family together as the difficult effects of the war persisted. With winter approaching, he was trying to keep his wife and children fed.

Until recently, there had been little thought in his mind of accepting any guests in his house. However, not long ago, as Mr. Rose sat in church one Sunday, listening to Chaplain Christof deliver the sermon, his views on the war began to change. In fact, it wasn't just about the war. It was about doing the right thing in life.

Chaplain Christof was speaking about the tragedy of orphaned children who needed safe hiding places during the occupation. It seemed to Mr. Rose that the chaplain was making subtle references to the plight of Jewish children. He couldn't come right out and say it but Mr. Rose understood what the chaplain was trying to tell his congregation.

Despite his personal struggles, Paul Rose felt like a rich man with a lot to offer. He came from a deeply religious Catholic family and felt that the intolerance of the Nazis was as much of an affront to their religion as it was to the Jews. He felt he had to take action.

After the service, Mr. Rose approached Chaplain Christof and arranged to help. Some people only felt comfortable taking a "white rabbit," a Jew who didn't look Jewish, because if the Germans discovered them, the consequences would not necessarily be so severe. Others, like Mr. Rose, decided to go a step further and take what they called a "black rabbit," a Jewish-looking *onderduiker,* like me. The risk was enormous for these families because if the Germans discovered them hiding a Jewish child in their home the consequences could be fatal.

Despite the danger, the Rose's home had become an underground safe house, where Dutch resistance fighters could find temporary food and shelter. On any given day, they showed up, exhausted, yet full of a passion to make the most of their lives.

I noticed right away that these university students were not like the rest of the townspeople. At a dining table made of thick oak planks, their conversation crackled, full of sharp humor and inside jokes. There was a constant stream of news about German targets bombed or another fellow rebel captured. Even though much of the news was bleak, they maintained an unbelievable optimism, as if there were no other way to see the world.

I was in awe of their courage and idealism. If I ever fought in a war, not just delivering cigarettes on my bicycle, these people were the soldiers I would like to join. Though most of them stayed just a few days, my situation was different. Mr. Rose told me I could stay as long as it was necessary, and that I should make it look like I belonged. That meant adjusting my biography and learning a few religious customs.

For example, if the milkman gave me a strange look when he saw me on his delivery, I should make the sign of the cross, which I learned to do quite convincingly, or so I was told. And if anyone asked, I was advised to say that I was from an adjacent village, and that my parents had been killed while working in a factory.

As I started all over again with a new family, I reminded myself about not becoming too comfortable in such a nice situation, because I knew it was probably only a matter of time before I'd be separated from these good people and back on my own.

44

Mr. Rose's daughter was beautiful, the same age as me, and as she led me to my new room on that first day, I found her hard to resist. Her blonde hair was loose and flowed halfway down her back, and she had a bright smile, which she shared with me the first moment we met. In the past year, I'd probably grown a couple inches and we were about the same height.

"Come on," Marta said. She beckoned me to come inside.

Intrigued, I sat on the edge of the bed and listened.

"A year ago, I woke up one morning to the sound of church bells ringing all over town. It wasn't a Sunday either, when the bells normally remind everyone to get to church. Our house was quiet. No one was moving about. I couldn't figure out why they kept on ringing the bells."

"A wedding?"

"Yes, I thought so at first, but who wants to get married in the middle of a war? Anyway, it could have been that, or even better, how about bells to ring in the end of the war?"

Marta flopped down on the bed beside me. Not only was she beautiful and smelled good; she was introspective and I liked that.

"Imagine that! The war ending on a bright and sunny Tuesday

morning in December. But then, my father told me it was the sound of protest."

"What do you mean?"

I forgot the protests I'd seen back long ago in Amsterdam, when local citizens gathered in the public squares, raising their voices to protest the German occupation.

"Many people here in Tegelen hate what's happening, and they don't want to keep quiet. Most of them, I'm sure."

Marta stood up and adjusted the curtains at the window. "Even though they can't speak up too loud or they risk being killed."

"That's true."

"We're so close to Germany here, you know, and when the invasion began, it was terrible. They came across the border and rolled over everything in sight, even animals. Anything in their way was shot or stolen or suffered some hideous punishment. We saw farm animals slaughtered for no reason and left in the road to rot. They just shot a dog if it got in the way of their trucks. They didn't care about anything." Marta's face turned pale as she told the story. "They were hideous. Even bicycles were stolen."

"In Amsterdam the Germans did that, too. They told us we couldn't ride our bikes anymore, and then they took them."

"They didn't tell us anything here. They only spoke with violence. At first, we were so shocked and frightened by how fast they were coming, and by the size and power of their army."

"But the Dutch army fought against them, didn't they?"

"In the beginning, they fought so hard, and for a couple of days, based on what we heard, we thought they had a chance. But we were kidding ourselves. At that time, the Nazis were impossible to defeat – and perhaps they still are, I don't know."

"Maybe it's better that the army surrendered so quickly before all of them were killed or taken as prisoners."

"And then killed. Yeah, they didn't have a chance. We lost a bunch of local men. Some were in the army, so they died fighting like soldiers do. One of our neighbors, a sweet Jewish man my father's age, he ran outside when the Nazis drove their vehicles through town and he yelled and screamed for them to go back to Germany, to leave us alone. He kept repeating that over and over."

"Oh my God."

I saw the tears in Marta's eyes.

"I'd never seen this man behave like that, so aggressive and crazy." As she went on, her voice tightened. "He must have felt completely desperate. The Germans didn't like what he was doing, and they hanged him from a tree right in front of his house. No one raised their voices anymore after that, at least not for a while."

"Oh Marta, I'm so sorry you had to see that."

"Yeah, it's been too much. Enough."

"What about the bells?"

"My father told me that ever since the Germans first invaded, there have been people resisting them. Sometimes, they do it in silence, and sometimes, like that day ringing the bells, they do it out loud, in public. Last year, when the people of Tegelen, the ones who were brave enough, decided to protest by ringing the church bells, I had no idea what the Germans would do. When my father gathered us together, we watched with the rest of the town as the Germans lowered the bells from every church tower in town, cut them loose, and hauled them away in their trucks. Once the bells got to Germany, they were melted down and turned into bullets."

"And those bullets come back here to shoot us, don't they?"

"I'm afraid you're right, Johannes."

For a moment, I didn't know who she was talking to. I turned to see if another person had walked in without me noticing. Then, I quickly remembered my new name, and that she was talking to me.

"The Germans are taking whatever they need to continue feeding their war machine, including the church bells. I wonder what they'll take next. They care for nothing. Johannes, you must be careful." She sounded stern but if I wasn't mistaken, her voice also said she liked me.

"You must listen to what my father tells you, and my mother too, and the resistance fighters when they pass through. Pay attention to them, and don't do anything foolish."

I looked at Marta, concerned because she was right, and smiling because I couldn't help myself. I wasn't a boy in the crèche anymore. I was a young man, stuck in the middle of a war, and happy to find a new friend, especially one as pretty and smart as Marta.

"Do you hear me?"

I nodded and smiled.

"The guys from the resistance say the Germans are trying to find every last Jew in the Netherlands, and once they catch them, they're all doomed to go to the concentration camps."

My smile disappeared.

But Marta's lecture didn't last long. It was Sunday, time to get ready for church. The Roses would spend the entire morning at mass, and I'd be on my own to enjoy some time alone. Most other days, I helped, undercover of course, which restricted most of my chores to inside the house and close by the Rose's property, where I could hide quickly if necessary.

45

September 5, 1944, marked nearly a year since I'd met Marta. As we stood outside the Rose's house that day, we couldn't believe our eyes. If there had been any church bells left in Tegelen, they would've all been ringing loudly. Everyone in the village thought the war was over, and we watched German soldiers run through the streets, retreating from the advancing Allied troops. People were keen to celebrate that morning, except those who had become German sympathizers. They were gathering whatever they could as fast as possible and preparing to escape. Tegelen was a village in chaos, and Marta and I asked anyone we could to explain what was happening.

According to Mr. Rose, one day earlier, the Allies, made up largely of American soldiers aided by British and French troops, had completed their occupation of neighboring Belgium, and it seemed certain that they'd be advancing into Germany in a matter of days, finally bringing the Nazis to their knees.

Back inside the house, we searched for more information. German radio stations said nothing about their retreat from Belgium. But according to British radio reports, which Dutch citizens were supposedly forbidden to listen to, the Allies might be sending troops through the Netherlands on their way to Germany.

When some resistance fighters came by, Marta and I insisted on them telling us everything they knew. No detail was too small. We wanted to know every nuance of what appeared to be the end of World War II. Those normally tight-lipped men and women were feeling particularly good on that Tuesday, and they shared quite a few stories.

They had seen Germans running around Tegelen, stealing anything they could, preferably anything on wheels, in a monumental effort to escape to their homeland. Dutch Nazis were also in a panic, realizing they'd better disappear before the tables were turned on them.

Still, the news wasn't all good. We weren't sure what was happening outside our area, so the good cheer was tempered with skepticism. The resistance fighters warned that the rumors of an imminent liberation might prove to be false, and the occupation would continue.

Nonetheless, rumors continued to fly throughout the day. Dutch radio announced that the liberation of Holland was about to begin. British reports grandly announced the end of the war, but an hour later they changed their tune, declaring the situation uncertain.

Mr. Rose, convinced the news was good, wanted to celebrate. He handed out glasses of beer to everyone in the kitchen and proposed that all of us drink to the crazy events of that Tuesday, what the Dutch still call *"Dolle Dinsdag"* or "Mad Tuesday," when our enemies, with the Allies fast approaching, lost their minds and ran away as fast as they could.

I longed to be Sal Kool again, no longer afraid of being exposed as a Jew, of being arrested and sent to a concentration camp. I vowed to return to Amsterdam somehow, by train, by bus or by catching a ride in a delivery truck. I didn't care how. I would have walked. Somehow, I'd get there, and so would every one of my family, and we'd all meet at home.

No such luck.

Over the next few days, the situation changed dramatically. The Germans regrouped along the Maas River, holding off the Allies' advance with heavy fighting. Everyone in Tegelen was on high alert, trapped between the river and the German border. Due to the heightened danger, I had to stay indoors, deep in hiding for the foreseeable future.

In a remarkably short time, I had gone from thinking I'd seen the war's end to being locked up inside a fight that seemed to never end. Life with the Roses was good but no matter how comfortable I had become, I never forgot the fact that I was separated from my own family.

46

Nothing much changed over the next few months. The war lumbered on, and while rumors kept flying that it could be over any day, the reality on the ground, at least in our area, was different. We had to remain vigilant, and I couldn't come out of hiding.

But on Christmas Eve, everyone in the Rose household was excited.

"Johannes, stand still! I can't fix your hair if you're fidgeting around."

"You're stabbing me with the hairpin, Marta."

"I'm making you beautiful for the first time in your life."

"Johannes, you're beautiful!" Bette, Marta's little sister, had to get into the act. "The boys will love you!"

I reached for Bette but she danced away. Both girls were giggling as they dressed me in their clothing. It was the only way Mr. Rose could be persuaded to let me join the family at church for mass. I was so happy to get out of the house for the first time in three months that I didn't mind masquerading as a girl, or the fact that I was about to attend a church mass for the first time in my life.

"This corduroy jumper looks so good on you," Marta said.

"Oh, it looks so good on you, oh my." Bette was making fun of Marta making fun of me.

"The white blouse makes the other colors stand out, don't you think?" Marta pinched her sister.

"Ouch! Yes! It does. It looks fantastic, okay? Leave me alone!"

"Marta, let her go. She's such a delicate little thing, remember?"

"Sure, my darling. I forgot how delicate you are."

Bette slapped Marta's hand away and sticked her tongue out at me. She was only 10 years old but she didn't tolerate anyone talking down to her.

"Like I said, the boys will love you, Johannes! Especially with that stupid kerchief on your head!"

I walked to the mirror and groaned. "It's horrible! Are you kidding me? I can't go like this."

"Johannes, if you want to get out this house, you'll wear it."

Bette had to chime in. "Come with us to church. You're so pretty! Everyone wants to see a pretty girl like you."

"Don't be so smart," said Marta. "We may be laughing now but once we set foot outside, it's serious business. If anyone recognizes Johannes, who knows what could happen?"

"But it's Christmas Eve! And we're going to church!"

"Yes, my dear, I know."

"Who would try to hurt Johannes if they found out?"

"Good question," I said, "but you never know during a war."

"Let's go. And remember, Bette, this is serious business."

Mr. Rose called out for us to join him for the walk to church. "Merry Christmas," he said, smiling, as we gathered at the front door. "You're quite a sight, Johannes. Good job, girls, he'll fit right in. And if you don't mind, let me do the talking, just in case anyone asks who you are or where you're from."

I nodded, nervous about the prospect of anyone speaking to me. We set out for church, greeting a few neighbors along the way who were also going to mass. No one said anything, at least not that I noticed. I kept my head down as we entered the candle-lit church. The sound of so many people singing was relaxing. Music can change things, I remembered. During all those years playing cello, I noticed that whenever I felt troubled, the music gave me a chance to escape into a more pleasant world where I could momentarily forget what was bothering me.

Now, despite the strange feeling of wearing a dress and being surrounded by crucifixes, I felt oddly at ease, enjoying the steady barrage of Christmas music. Some of the songs sounded vaguely familiar from hearing them years ago in school.

"It's nice, isn't it?" Marta whispered, careful to keep us safe.

I nodded, afraid to use my voice. "Beautiful," I mouthed.

"Are you referring to me, or the music?"

"What?" I couldn't believe Marta was flirting with me, right there in the church and while I was dressed as a girl.

"You heard me." Marta smiled. "So, what's your answer?"

"Oh, you know." I felt my face blush.

"Tell me later. It's time to get up and go."

"Go? Where?"

"Down to the altar, silly girl. Join us for communion."

Mr. Rose was already moving out of the pew, hand in hand with Bette. Marta followed, and as she looked back, she saw me staying behind. She nodded ever so slightly for me to join her but I was afraid to move, for fear of being discovered. Marta nodded again, a bit more insistently. Everyone was lining up to go to the altar and into the booths at the front of the sanctuary. I had no idea what communion meant or what people were doing inside those little booths. I thought everyone must be eating a little snack and going to the toilet. I didn't want to stick out by not complying with the rules of the church.

When it was my turn, I took a wafer in my mouth as quickly as I could before the priest recognized me. Then I stepped inside one of the booths and closed the door. It was dark and I couldn't see a toilet anywhere. I jumped when a voice came out of the darkness.

"Johannes, go ahead, you can go back."

I had no idea who was there, or how he recognized me.

"Really, Johannes, you don't have to stay."

I couldn't speak. I left the booth, still not sure if it had a toilet.

Later, back in the Rose's house, I found out that the voice belonged to Chaplain Christof, and that the booth was only used for confession. Although I had enjoyed getting out of the house for a short while, I knew it had been a unique opportunity that I couldn't risk again.

Winter was taking hold, and food was becoming scarce. As war supplies were further depleted, the German army's search for forced labor intensified. With their military situation worsening, the Nazis hunt for resistance fighters and Jews in hiding grew more desperate and violent. As long as the situation continued, I would have to remain inside the Rose's house.

47

On New Year's morning 1945, I found Mr. Rose in the kitchen, cutting a hole in the floor.

"What on earth are you doing?"

"Ah, Happy New Year, Johannes. I hope I'm saving your life!"

"What do you mean?"

"You know how bad it's been getting, with soldiers barging into people's houses whenever they get the urge."

"Yeah, of course. Every time they come here, I hide and pray they won't search too carefully."

"Exactly. We've been lucky till now, so that's why I'm installing a trapdoor here, hidden in the floorboards in case of emergency. Let's see if you can fit through the hole I made."

"I'll try it, I guess."

Mr. Rose could sense my hesitation. "I'm sorry, Johannes, but you have to. The risk is too great without it."

Even though I'd grown considerably since my gymnastics days, I was still quite agile and flexible. The hole wasn't large, so those qualities helped. I slid my legs under the floorboards and shimmied into the crawl space up to my shoulders. Only my head remained exposed.

"Okay, Johannes, that's good. You feel okay in there?"

"It's quite snug, but I'm fine."

"Well, now comes the hard part. I'm sorry about this but you should be able to breathe under there. The floorboards aren't airtight, that's for sure."

"What if they are?"

"Don't worry. After I close you in, I'll wait here and see how you're doing. Just yell if you can't breathe."

He replaced the trap door among the floorboards, closing me in completely under the kitchen floor. At first, it felt like the kind of prank I might've tried with Louis back in our house, if we had ever had the courage to try it.

Soon enough, though, I began to panic. "Mr. Rose? Are you there?"

"Of course I am. How do you feel?"

"Like I'm buried alive."

"Yeah, I'm not surprised. Sorry for that. But can you breathe?"

"Yeah, if I can relax, I guess I can breathe."

"Well, that's what you have to do in case they ever come. Now, let's get you out."

I was relieved to stand on my own two feet. I hoped I would never have to crawl under there again, especially with real soldiers right over my head, searching for me.

48

"Hurry!"

Marta grabbed my arm as Mr. Rose yanked me out of my chair, slid it out of the way, and pushed me under the table.

"They're coming!"

Bette ran to her lookout by the window. We all heard voices approaching and the sound of boots banging on the wooden pallets outside the door. The unscheduled visit had caught us by surprise, interrupting our dinner and forcing me to open the trapdoor as fast as I could and squeeze myself into the improvised hiding place.

"It's okay, Johannes," Marta said. "They won't stay long."

I heard the boots enter the kitchen. The Germans shuffled around and asked questions. Apparently, they thought that Mr. Rose might be hiding someone. While they interrogated the family, I kept as still as I could, too petrified to breathe, straining to find a peaceful thought to hold onto. Each time there was silence, I begged someone to speak, just to cover any sound my breath might make. The Roses were good actors because a few minutes later, the Germans were gone. Life could resume as normal.

These visits continued for several weeks. They always seemed to come during our evening meal. By the fourth or fifth time the

Germans interrupted us, I was used to the routine. One time, I even took my supper plate with me to finish my meal quietly, lying in the dark.

49

As winter turned to spring, and Holland's famous tulips began to bloom, the war seemed to be getting worse. The temperature was rising, and so was the frequency of the Allied bombing campaign. We heard and sometimes saw American and British planes flying overhead on an hourly basis, en route to Germany, just kilometers away. The tide was turning, faster and faster, and we hoped it was just a matter of time before the Nazis folded.

Marta and I discussed this every night, and we prayed for the war to end. Our unusual friendship had developed into something deeper over the winter. Meeting in wartime affected both of us, and as teenagers we had a lot to figure out. We were still children, scared and lonely, and we were also becoming young adults, with growing bodies and new ideas. We began to spend nights together in the same bed, as much for the emotional connection as the warmth and excitement of each other's bodies. I felt free with Marta in ways I'd never imagined. For the first time in my life, I had someone I could really talk to, someone I could trust with my most private thoughts. Most nights, we shared our dreams of the future and what we would do when the war was over.

"Tell me a story."

This was Marta's familiar line as we listened to the planes flying overhead.

"Like what?"

"From your childhood, before I knew you."

"Okay. Let me think."

"Don't think. Just tell."

"When I was 11 years old," I said, "I was coming out of school one day, and a girl in my class handed me a small booklet. She made me hold it in my hand and then she ran away. I had no idea what it was or why she had given it to me."

"What was it?"

"I don't know. It's silly, really."

"Silly? Oh, thank goodness. We need something silly."

"Never mind." I tried to change the subject. "I'll rub your feet. They look cold."

"You will not!"

Marta kicked me gently with one of her feet.

"Tell me!"

"It was a sex manual."

"What? A manual for sex! Shocking!"

"Ha ha, very funny."

"I hid it under my sweater because I surely wasn't going to throw it away."

"I should hope not. After all, you were a healthy 11-year-old boy, right?"

I nodded, laughing.

"I went home with it hidden under my sweater because I didn't want my mother to find it. She would've told my father, and I would've been in big trouble."

"So, what did you do?"

"I put it under the covers of my bed. Later, when my mother came to say goodnight, I was so nervous, thinking she would find it."

"And?"

"She said goodnight, and nothing happened. The next morning, when I was getting dressed to go to school, I couldn't figure out what to do with the manual. I couldn't leave it at home. My mother might clean my room and find it."

"So, where'd you leave it?"

"I put it back under my sweater."

"To keep it warm?"

"Ha ha, yes. And then, in my rush to get to school on time, I dropped it in the middle of the kitchen floor."

"Oh my God! Your mother must've seen it. What did she do?"

"She didn't see it at first, so I picked it up and tucked it inside a piece of a newspaper and rushed off to school, not realizing it had fallen on the floor before I got out the door."

"Uh oh! That's big trouble!"

"I had to sweat it out all day in school, wondering what she was going to tell my father when he got home from work that night."

"What happened?"

"She didn't say a word, at first. A little later, when I thought I might've escaped any consequences, my father called me to come meet his guests. I was already in my pajamas. I was ready to kiss him goodnight and go back to my room. Suddenly, he took out the manual and showed it to everyone, as if it were something to celebrate."

"Oh no."

"Then he says to his friends, 'One of Sal's classmates gave him this wonderful book! What a lovely friend you have. You know, my son, this is just the first book in a whole series. Why don't I get you the other parts for your birthday?'"

"He really said that?"

"I was so embarrassed. My father didn't have an ounce of anger in him about me having that little sex book. Entirely the opposite! He couldn't have been any nicer. And funny, too, I must admit, even though it didn't feel that way at the time."

"Oh, that's a beautiful story."

"I miss my father."

Marta was silent, and soon we fell asleep.

50

Chaplain Christof came to speak with me. We sat alone in the kitchen, where everything important in the Rose household took place – meals, fights, late night stories, business transactions, and more meals – all at the large, wooden table.

"Johannes, the war will end any day now. It's a sure thing this time."

"How can you be so certain?"

"I pray to God every day for good news but I don't get my war reports from him." The chaplain was a kind man who had always been good to me. I could trust him and the information he provided. "The radio station in London says that Berlin has been occupied by the Russian army and the Germans there have surrendered. They have also surrendered to the Allies in Italy, and soon it will happen here, too."

"It's true, isn't it?" I could hardly move.

"Now that the war is about to end, you must reconsider your position in the world."

"What do you mean?"

"Times have changed. What the Germans have done in Europe is so enormous that life may never be the same again for any of us. I've thought about your situation for a long time."

I leaned in closer, as if his every word could change my life.

"When the war ends, it would be much easier if you became a Catholic. It's not so difficult to do."

I could hardly believe what I was hearing. My head got hot, and my cheeks flushed. "I don't know. I don't know about that. I'll have to ask my parents about that when they come back, and then I'll let you know. I'll let you know, Chaplain Christof, okay?"

He stared at me and reached his hand across the table.

"Johannes, your parents may not be coming back."

I looked at this man across the table and wondered how he could say such a thing.

"Of course, they'll come back. What are you talking about? "

Chaplain Christof cleared his throat, as if he were about to say something.

"How can you know that? You're here in one little corner of the Netherlands. There's a lot of other places they could be right now, so how could you have any idea where they are?"

He said nothing.

I continued, declaring what I thought was the only possible truth. "Once this war ends, they'll come back and we'll meet at home in Amsterdam."

"I hope you're right."

"I know I'm right!"

After the Chaplain said goodbye, I kept repeating this to myself.

For a long time after he left, I stayed in the kitchen, unable to move or face any possibility other than seeing my family again. Then, without realizing it, I began to pray, for the first time in years, maybe for the first time in my life.

51

I woke up early the next day and went into the kitchen, expecting to be alone. It was May 5, my 18th birthday, and I planned to start it by myself with a cup of coffee, just as I had done when I turned 16. Hopefully, there would be no German soldiers knocking on the door this time.

"Happy Birthday to you..."

I heard voices singing in the darkness.

"Happy Birthday, dear Johannes. Happy Birthday to you!"

As I turned on the light, I saw Mr. Rose, his wife, Marta, and Bette.

"Thanks, I never expected you to be awake so early."

"A birthday comes just once a year."

"Yeah, you're right. When I turned 13, it was an important birthday, a big one for a Jewish boy. My mother made sure the whole family was there. A year later, the situation in Amsterdam made it impossible to do anything."

"Nothing's changed, really."

Mrs. Rose brought a small plate of food to the table.

"When I turned 16, first thing in the morning, just like now, the German police took me away from where I was hiding."

"You were all alone on your birthday?" Bette sounded shocked at the idea. "That's mean!"

"You're right. It was. And since then, nothing has been normal."

"Johannes," Mr. Rose said, "what is normal for any of us, anymore?"

A few hours later, as we gathered to eat a simple lunch, two members of the resistance ran inside the house, interrupting our meal with an astonishing announcement: "The German army has surrendered to the Allies!"

"Yes! It's true! It's over. The surrender is final!"

We were stunned to hear those words spoken out loud.

"The war is over, once and for all!"

"There's no mistake this time, like we made before. It's now official."

None of us could speak. We weren't sure if we believed the news but we were desperate to accept it as the truth. Could it be true? Finally?

Tears ran down Mr. Rose's face. Marta looked at me with joy and sadness and a mix of emotion I couldn't understand. I could hardly breathe. It was like someone was offering me a fantastic present and I didn't know how to accept it.

On May 5, 1945, exactly five years after the Germans took control of our country, I would finally get to watch them go home. Five years of this wretched war would be over.

I tried to stand, but my legs had frozen. As I began to comprehend the news, my stomach began to turn upside down. After such a long time, the prospect of seeing my family again, or finding out they were lost forever, was too much to process.

From one minute to the next, everything was changing, and I felt more out of control than ever. I became dizzy and short of breath. My whole body was heating up. I was becoming sick, so I forced myself to get up from the table.

I ran outside and vomited.

52

"It's time for me to go."

I stood outside, a few days after Germany had officially surrendered to the Allies, with no idea how to say goodbye to the Rose family.

"It's safe for you now, Johannes. You should find your way home."

"That's where I belong, right?"

"Yes, you should go to Amsterdam."

"I have no idea where my family has gone. I don't even know if they're still alive."

"I really hope they are." Mr. Rose put his hands on my shoulders. "Have you told Marta you're leaving?"

"She knows I will eventually. I'm not anxious to say goodbye to her but I have to. You understand, don't you?"

"Yes, I do."

"It's strange to leave all of you, and Tegelen. Amsterdam feels so far away, like a completely different lifetime for me. I don't know what I'm returning to."

"You'll figure it out soon enough." Mr. Rose tried to reassure me that everything would work out. "Find Marta before you go. You must do that."

"Of course. She is important to me."

He nodded. "I know you've been good to my daughter."

"Mr. Rose, how can I ever thank you for what you've done? I have no idea what to say now. You and your family, you saved my life. You know that, don't you?"

"You're a good boy, Johannes. A man, really. You've become a man in this short time. But you needn't say any more right now. We've only done what's right, and I wish we could do more to help you get back home."

"You've done so much."

"Thank you. Your words mean a great deal."

"I wish I could give you something."

"There's something I want to give you."

I looked at Mr. Rose, unsure of what he meant.

"I want to give you back your name. So, go now, Sal. Go home, Salomon Kool and find your life again." He turned away and headed toward the house.

I was stunned to hear my name again. Another gift I didn't know how to accept. "Will your family be okay?"

"Don't worry about us. As soon as we get some food growing in the backyard, we'll be in good shape. You just take care of yourself and don't look back."

"But I can visit you." I already felt sorry for leaving.

"Listen, Sal, don't look back. No matter what happens, don't look back. Something unbelievable has happened here, and you'll need all your energy to put your life back together."

I nodded as Mr. Rose patted me on the back and went inside the house. It wasn't long before Marta came outside. We looked at each other for a long time before she spoke.

"Johannes, it's okay. You must go. And go now. Don't wait."

"You're right, Marta. I have to but..."

Marta motioned for me to stop talking. "My older sister has this baby. I never told you she's a foster baby, a Jewish child they've been protecting this entire time until the war ends. And now that it is over, what will they do? What will any of us do?"

"I don't know, Marta. No one has to hide anymore."

"Maybe my sister will never return this baby. I'm afraid she might not. What about the baby, then? And its parents?"

"What about the parents? Who knows if they're even still alive?"

"Oh God, you're right. There must be orphans everywhere right now, wondering if their parents will ever return."

"I could be one of them."

Marta took my hand. "You're free now. You must go and find out about your family."

"Yes, I'm free. But free to do what?"

"To find the truth, whether you want to know it or not."

She was right. I had to return immediately to Amsterdam.

"Go now, my dear Salomon Kool, big-city boy from Amsterdam."

I felt torn. I think I knew real love for the first time, and I was looking at her.

"Don't look back, Sal."

"Your father said that..."

"I know."

"I'll never forget you."

"No, you won't." She shook her head. "We will never forget."

53

I left Tegelen that afternoon and headed home – if Amsterdam could be considered that again. On the way, I got off the train in Eindhoven, where we'd lived before the war. The last time I'd been there was with Louis, that day we rode our bicycles all the way from Amsterdam.

I had no idea what to expect. Throughout the train ride from Tegelen, I tried to imagine it but I couldn't predict what the mood in the city would be, or how many people might be there, returning to their homes. I thought about all the Jews who had been forced to ride trains from there to the camps. I had watched them being taken from The Jewish Theater across the street from the crèche. Now, I wondered how many would return.

As I left the station, I discovered the central square of Eindhoven overflowing with people, searching for familiar faces of lost loved ones.

Relief. Exhaustion. Fear. Hope. Love. All those emotions were on display. Everyone was just glad to be alive, having suffered through these terrible years, some in hiding, some returning from concentration camps, and now, exhausted from their experience and wondering what would happen next. Each survivor looked frightened, hoping against hope to reunite with their loved ones.

I scanned the crowd for a familiar face, not sure if I would even recognize my own father, or mother, or brothers and sister among all the gaunt, grey faces. It looked as if the war had changed everyone, and not for the better.

I came across a group of children huddled nearby who had just been liberated from the Bergen-Belsen concentration camp in Germany. They seemed overwhelmed, as if they were living half a life, stuck awake in a nightmare. I wasn't sure if they even realized where they were, and that they were no longer imprisoned in the camp.

In the midst of the children, enthusiastically organizing them, stood a surprisingly energetic middle-aged man, who looked vaguely familiar. I saw it was Ernst Feldmann, a friend of my father's, and the uncle of my best friend, Frank.

I thought that if Mr. Feldmann was there, maybe my father was too. And maybe Frank was there, looking for me all this time. I figured that Mr. Feldmann had the answers to my questions. He would know about my family.

I maneuvered through the crowd, pushing people aside when I had to, until I reached him. "Mr. Feldmann, I can't believe it's you." Though I was excited to see a familiar face, I was nervous that he might carry bad news.

"Sal, is it you? Salomon Kool? I'm so glad you are okay. My God, you've grown. The Nazis couldn't stop that, could they?"

Feldmann explained that he had also survived the war in hiding, moving from house to house in Amsterdam, and when that was no longer safe, he had headed south, where he stayed in a series of safe houses until the war was over.

Feeling lucky to be alive and to be healthy in body and spirit, Feldmann was helping the Red Cross reunite these children with their relatives, whenever possible, back in Amsterdam.

"Excuse me but have you seen my parents? Or my brothers or my sister? Have you seen any of them?"

"No, Sal, I'm so sorry, I don't have any idea where they are." He shook his head as he looked at me. "I can't help you, I'm sorry."

"Nothing?"

"Not a clue, I'm afraid."

"What about Frank? Any word?"

"No. No word yet. I'm afraid it doesn't look good."

I waited a second, hoping he might remember something. "Well, thanks anyway, Mr. Feldmann. Good to see you're okay."

"Sal, wait, please. These children need help, and who knows? You might meet someone who has information about your family."

"What shall I do?"

"Get on one of the buses with those children, over there." He pointed to a group of children across the square.

"Next to the fountain, go with them to the Red Cross center in Amsterdam. Word has gone out that people should collect family members there when they arrive. The Red Cross is telling everyone. Maybe your family will find you there, too."

As Mr. Feldmann explained the situation, it sank in even more that the war had ended, and I would see my family soon. I felt almost giddy with anticipation. The German occupation was over. I expected to return to my old neighborhood and find it as it was before the war.

I gathered the children together and helped them board the buses. There were so many! Before we left Eindhoven, we stopped at several local homes for something to eat, all arranged by the wonderful workers of the Red Cross.

My bus arrived at the same house where Louis and I had spent the night a long time ago when we defied our mother and cycled 130 kilometers away from home. When I brought some of the children inside this familiar house, I had a sweet reunion with the Vissers.

One child grabbed a piece of chocolate off the table and put it in his pocket. I realized that the young boy must've barely survived. Although I was happy to see these children alive, their condition and the uncertainties ahead made me sad. My feeling of guilt was even stronger as it washed over me for the first time. I had escaped the horrors of the camps, while this child grabbing the chocolate, and all the others too, had gone to one of the camps instead of me. They had taken my place in what must've been an absolute hell of an existence.

While I was boarding the bus that would take us to Amsterdam, I recognized Sam Kluivert, Frank's younger brother. Sam was staring at some black-and-white photos of the liberation of the concentration camps. "That was me," he said, pointing to a photograph of a large hole, surrounded by a group of boys, using shovels to fill it with corpses.

That was all he said.

I was speechless. I realized that nothing would ever be the same again.

54

On September 5, 1945, I returned to Amsterdam. By the time our bus reached the outer ring of the city, most of the children were asleep but I was restless and wide awake. I had no one who might be there to greet the bus, or if anyone knew I was on it. *Would anyone from my family be back yet? Could they have found each other and now come to find me?* These thoughts rushed through my mind so I could barely sit still.

"I don't know where I'll sleep tonight."

No one noticed me muttering to myself.

"What if they don't come back? What will I do?"

I felt an overpowering sense of disbelief, just considering that possibility. Five people couldn't be erased off the earth. I knew they were on the way. If not today, they'd be back soon.

When a Red Cross volunteer asked me to help wake the children, it came as a welcome distraction, helping me to forget my own anxieties. In a few minutes, we'd be at the Portugeesch Israelitisch Ziekenhuis, a hospital used as the meeting point place for what everyone hoped would become the scene of joyous family reunions.

"Just wait," a volunteer said. "Someone will be there for you. Everything will work out."

I nodded in agreement, half of me believing it was true, while the other half tried to convince me that everything would work out. "You're right. It'll be fine." I didn't trust my own voice but I was full of hope, nonetheless.

A crowd of adults were waiting, looking anxiously to see their children step off the bus and into their open arms. I watched many children reunite with their loved ones – some mothers, a few fathers, but mostly older siblings and cousins. I heard so many asking for their parents. I couldn't imagine what they were being told. At first, I was happy to see everyone come together, but I couldn't help thinking of myself and finding my own family.

I searched through the crowd, asking everyone I could. I didn't find anyone who knew my parents, let alone had any news of them. The Red Cross couldn't offer any suggestions.

The crowd began to thin. I remembered how lost I once felt in a large city like Amsterdam. So many Jews had once lived there but I didn't know many of them. Now, no one wanted to hear about what I'd suffered. Everyone had terrible things to tell, and who wanted to think of them anymore?

I stood alone in the middle of the street. Even though I was back on my own turf, the anxiety and fear I had felt, hiding from the Germans, took hold once again. I had no idea what to do, but I knew I had to move. Nothing would come from standing still. Perhaps if I kept moving, I'd run into someone I knew.

As I walked toward my old neighborhood, I passed a few familiar landmarks. The crèche was still there, ghostly quiet and abandoned. The Jewish Theater also looked deserted. I felt as if the months I'd spent there existed in another lifetime, and I had no desire to revisit what offered me absolutely nothing.

I kept on walking, constantly on the lookout for a familiar face. I passed by my old school, the one I attended in happier days, before I'd been forced to go to east Amsterdam and join a Jewish-only academy. Nothing had changed on the outside. The children's drawings hanging on the windows gave me a small feeling of hope.

I remembered many of my old classmates and wondered if any of them were still around, about to bump into me and deliver news of my family. I lingered around in the playground area, hoping I was right, but I saw no one I knew.

I noticed an old familiar shop nearby. It appeared to have been shut down long ago, yet I could see a name etched into a pane of glass, still intact on the front door. The shop had once been Koco's ice cream parlor, and I thought of its former owner, Ernst Cahn, and how he had been brutally murdered.

As I peered inside, I thought I caught a glimpse of my father. It was my own reflection in the glass door, a young man, taller than I'd been the last time I stood there. I looked relatively young, between a boy and a man. I saw a face full of fear and uncertainty.

I turned away, but immediately was drawn to look again. Maybe if I looked deeper inside the shop, I might see my father sitting there. Of course, I wasn't only wrong. I was going crazy, and I knew I had to pull myself together. Everything I'd been through since my family broke apart was rushing through my head. Each time someone disappeared – first Daniel, then Louis, and Tinie soon after, and then my father, and finally that day the Germans took my mother and my aunt. As each of them vanished, so did a piece of my childhood.

The war shattered everything I thought my life would become. After all the years of instability and uncertainty, I wasn't sure how I could put it back together. At that moment, alone in Amsterdam, with no idea what would happen, I knew I had to stop thinking about the past. My only option was to move on and make something new.

I had to start right away as I walked toward my old neighborhood.

I am a survivor, and I am going home. I am going home to find my family.

EPILOGUE

Sal moved in with his only surviving cousin immediately after the war. He began studying physical therapy but the Dutch mandatory military draft cut that short. Sal tried to secure an exemption, appealing all the way to the top of the government, to the Queen herself, claiming that as a Holocaust survivor he should have special consideration. He was denied.

The army sent Sal to the Dutch East Indies, now Indonesia, in October 1947. When he returned, two-and-a-half years later, he joined the Jewish War Orphans' Organization, however he was disappointed because they didn't do much to help him.

Back in Amsterdam, Sal joined a group of survivors, called the Magen David Club. He met Nettie Blitz, a strong, beautiful woman who had also survived the war in hiding, thanks to Walter Süskind. She was the first person in a very long time that Sal truly trusted. In 1954, Sal and Nettie were married. They had two sons, who now live in Israel with their families.

For years, Sal never stopped hoping that his parents, his two brothers, and his sister were still alive. He searched endlessly through hundreds of documents and dozens of microfilm records from the war.

Eventually, Sal learned the following from Red Cross records:

- September 30, 1942: Sal's brother, Louis, died in Auschwitz.
- March 31, 1943: Sal's father, Philip, died in Auschwitz.
- April 2, 1943: Sal's mother, Rachel, and his sister, Tinie, died in Sobibor.
- April 30, 1943: Sal's brother, Daniel, died in Auschwitz.

For the rest of his life, Salomon Kool remained haunted by memories of his family. He carried the burden of what is called survivor's guilt: that he escaped the worst, while his family suffered and died.

Salomon Kool died in Amsterdam on April 18, 2011. He was 83 years old. His wife, Nettie, still lives in Amsterdam, and his sons, Robert and Philip, live in Israel.

You can learn more about Salomon Kool in a 2005 documentary film, *Secret Courage: The Walter Süskind Story*, where Sal and other children describe how Süskind saved them.

As Sal said, "You will come over it, but you never forget it. You live with it, and you go dying with it. And you never forget."

ACKNOWLEDGMENTS

My thanks to Sandy Batkin, who first invited me to write this story, and put me on a plane to Amsterdam, where I was fortunate to spend such a meaningful week with Sal and Nettie Kool and begin a lovely relationship with both of them. Thanks to my literary agent, Nancy Rosenfeld, for representing me and this story, and to Liesbeth Heenk and Amsterdam Publishers, for providing the opportunity to reach a larger audience. I also appreciate the help I received from the United States Holocaust Memorial Museum, the Museum of Jewish Heritage and the National Holocaust Museum in Amsterdam.

As the son of a cantor, who served in WWII, I grew up in the shadows of the Holocaust, and would like to recognize those in my family who perished during the war, along with the millions of others we never had the pleasure to know.

Finally, loving thanks to my children, Max and Stella.

ABOUT THE AUTHOR

David is a writer, editor, and performing artist, based in New York City. His memoir, *American Misfit*, was released in 2017.

He is the co-author of several books about cancer, including *Rx for Hope, Reimagining Women's Cancers and Reimagining Men's Cancers, The Cancer Book: 101 Stories of Courage, Support and Love* and the author of *Write for Life: Communicating Your Way Through Cancer*. He coauthored *The Intelligent Divorce, The Wright Choice: Your Family's Guide to Healthy Eating, Modern Fitness and Saving Money*, and was consulting editor for Marlo Thomas and her *New York Times* bestseller *The Right Words at the Right Time, Volume 2: Your Turn*.

David has performed as an actor, clown and juggler, at Lincoln Center, Radio City Music Hall, the Beacon Theatre and throughout the United States and Europe, most notably at the Edinburgh Fringe

Festival, where THE STAGE wrote, "He is a supremely skillful performer and fine actor, reaching levels no other comics have matched at this Fringe."

Please visit www.tabatsky.com.

AMSTERDAM PUBLISHERS HOLOCAUST LIBRARY

The series **Holocaust Survivor Memoirs World War II** consists of the following autobiographies of survivors:

Outcry. Holocaust Memoirs, by Manny Steinberg

Hank Brodt Holocaust Memoirs. A Candle and a Promise, by Deborah Donnelly

The Dead Years. Holocaust Memoirs, by Joseph Schupack

Rescued from the Ashes. The Diary of Leokadia Schmidt, Survivor of the Warsaw Ghetto, by Leokadia Schmidt

My Lvov. Holocaust Memoir of a twelve-year-old Girl, by Janina Hescheles

Remembering Ravensbrück. From Holocaust to Healing, by Natalie Hess

Wolf. A Story of Hate, by Zeev Scheinwald with Ella Scheinwald

Save my Children. An Astonishing Tale of Survival and its Unlikely Hero, by Leon Kleiner with Edwin Stepp

Holocaust Memoirs of a Bergen-Belsen Survivor & Classmate of Anne Frank, by Nanette Blitz Konig

Defiant German - Defiant Jew. A Holocaust Memoir from inside the Third Reich, by Walter Leopold with Les Leopold

In a Land of Forest and Darkness. The Holocaust Story of two Jewish Partisans, by Sara Lustigman Omelinski

Holocaust Memories. Annihilation and Survival in Slovakia, by Paul Davidovits

From Auschwitz with Love. The Inspiring Memoir of Two Sisters' Survival, Devotion and Triumph Told by Manci Grunberger Beran & Ruth Grunberger Mermelstein, by Daniel Seymour

Remetz. Resistance Fighter and Survivor of the Warsaw Ghetto, by Jan Yohay Remetz

My March Through Hell. A Young Girl's Terrifying Journey to Survival, by Halina Kleiner with Edwin Stepp

---

The series **Holocaust Survivor True Stories WWII** consists of the following biographies:

Among the Reeds. The true story of how a family survived the Holocaust, by Tammy Bottner

A Holocaust Memoir of Love & Resilience. Mama's Survival from Lithuania to America, by Ettie Zilber

Living among the Dead. My Grandmother's Holocaust Survival Story of Love and Strength, by Adena Bernstein Astrowsky

Heart Songs. A Holocaust Memoir, by Barbara Gilford

Shoes of the Shoah. The Tomorrow of Yesterday, by Dorothy Pierce

Hidden in Berlin. A Holocaust Memoir, by Evelyn Joseph Grossman

Separated Together. The Incredible True WWII Story of Soulmates Stranded an Ocean Apart, by Kenneth P. Price, Ph.D.

The Man Across the River. The incredible story of one man's will to survive the Holocaust, by Zvi Wiesenfeld

If Anyone Calls, Tell Them I Died. A Memoir, by Emanuel (Manu) Rosen

The House on Thrömerstrasse. A Story of Rebirth and Renewal in the Wake of the Holocaust, by Ron Vincent

Dancing with my Father. His hidden past. Her quest for truth. How Nazi Vienna shaped a family's identity, by Jo Sorochinsky

The Story Keeper. Weaving the Threads of Time and Memory - A Memoir, by Fred Feldman

Krisia's Silence. The Girl who was not on Schindler's List, by Ronny Hein

Defying Death on the Danube. A Holocaust Survival Story, by Debbie J. Callahan with Henry Stern

A Doorway to Heroism. A decorated German-Jewish Soldier who became an American Hero, by Rabbi W. Jack Romberg

The Shoemaker's Son. The Life of a Holocaust Resister, by Laura Beth Bakst

The Redhead of Auschwitz. A True Story, by Nechama Birnbaum

Land of Many Bridges. My Father's Story, by Bela Ruth Samuel Tenenholtz

Creating Beauty from the Abyss. The Amazing Story of Sam Herciger, Auschwitz Survivor and Artist, by Lesley Ann Richardson

On Sunny Days We Sang. A Holocaust Story of Survival and Resilience, by Jeannette Grunhaus de Gelman

Painful Joy. A Holocaust Family Memoir, by Max J. Friedman

I Give You My Heart. A True Story of Courage and Survival, by Wendy Holden

In the Time of Madmen, by Mark A. Prelas

Monsters and Miracles. Horror, Heroes and the Holocaust, by Ira Wesley Kitmacher

Flower of Vlora. Growing up Jewish in Communist Albania, by Anna Kohen

Aftermath: Coming of Age on Three Continents. A Memoir, by Annette Libeskind Berkovits

Not a real Enemy. The True Story of a Hungarian Jewish Man's Fight for Freedom, by Robert Wolf

The Glassmaker's Son. Looking for the World my Father left behind in Nazi Germany, by Peter Kupfer

Zaidy's War, by Martin Bodek

The Apprentice of Buchenwald. The True Story of the Teenage Boy Who Sabotaged Hitler's War Machine, by Oren Schneider

---

The series **Jewish Children in the Holocaust** consists of the following autobiographies of Jewish children hidden during WWII in the Netherlands:

Searching for Home. The Impact of WWII on a Hidden Child, by Joseph Gosler

See You Tonight and Promise to be a Good Boy! War memories, by Salo Muller

Sounds from Silence. Reflections of a Child Holocaust Survivor, Psychiatrist and Teacher, by Robert Krell

Sabine's Odyssey. A Hidden Child and her Dutch Rescuers, by Agnes Schipper

The Journey of a Hidden Child, by Harry Pila with Robin Black

---

The series **New Jewish Fiction** consists of the following novels, written by Jewish authors. All novels are set in the time during or after the Holocaust.

The Corset Maker. A Novel, by Annette Libeskind Berkovits

Escaping the Whale. The Holocaust is over. But is it ever over for the next generation? by Ruth Rotkowitz

When the Music Stopped. Willy Rosen's Holocaust, by Casey Hayes

Hands of Gold. One Man's Quest to Find the Silver Lining in Misfortune, by Roni Robbins

The Girl Who Counted Numbers. A Novel, by Roslyn Bernstein

There was a garden in Nuremberg. A Novel, by Navina Michal Clemerson

The Butterfly and the Axe, by Omer Bartov

Good For a Single Journey, by Helen Joyce

The series **Holocaust Books for Young Adults** consists of the following novels, based on true stories:

The Boy behind the Door. How Salomon Kool Escaped the Nazis. Inspired by a True Story, by David Tabatsky

Running for Shelter. A True Story, by Suzette Sheft

The Precious Few. An Inspirational Saga of Courage based on True Stories, by David Twain with Art Twain

Jacob's Courage: A Holocaust Love Story, by Charles S. Weinblatt

---

The series **WW2 Historical Fiction** consists of the following novels, some of which are based on true stories:

Mendelevski's Box. A Heartwarming and Heartbreaking Jewish Survivor's Story, by Roger Swindells

A Quiet Genocide. The Untold Holocaust of Disabled Children WW2 Germany, by Glenn Bryant

The Knife-Edge Path, by Patrick T. Leahy

Want to be an AP book reviewer?

Reviews are very important in a world dominated by the social media and social proof. Please drop us a line if you want to join the *AP review team*. We will then add you to our list of advance reviewers. No strings attached, and we promise that we will not be spamming you.

info@amsterdampublishers.com